GAN LADY

ELLEN CANNON

YELLOW BRICK PUBLISHERS

First Published 1993 by

YELLOW BRICK PUBLISHERS. 2, LONSDALE
ROAD. QUEENS PARK. LONDON . NW6 6 RD.

British Library Cataloguing in Publication Data A
catalogue record for this book is available from the
British Library.

ISBN: 0-9520560-0-3

Typeset by Lonsdale Press Ltd
Printed and bound in Great Britain by
Cox & Wyman Ltd, Reading

FOREWORD

When I 'went respectable' or, in other words, when my husband gave up robbing banks and other villainy in favour of earning a living by writing, I was often asked what it had been like, married to a man who had spent a lot of his life behind bars. This set me to thinking. All my life I have been a great reader but I cannot remember ever coming across a book that told the story of the woman who was referred to as 'er indoors' long before the phrase was used by Arthur Daley in a television series.

First off I could have said that she spent the greater part of her time being a wife and mother in circumstances varying between extreme comfort and dire poverty. When my man was doing the business the family wanted for nothing. The first duty of a villain is to put money indoors when he is at liberty. He should also leave something behind when the law catches up with him, though this is not always possible due to unforeseen circumstances such as being nicked bang to rights. In rare cases, where a police marksman puts an end to a villain's career, there is always the widow's pension, though it's cold comfort.

There are exceptions to the general rule. A few of the top jollies, having pulled off a big job, retire to sunnier climes, often taking with them some bimbo who cops for the lot while 'er indoors is left with the bits and pieces and the memories of past good times. There are certain duties which the villain's wife must perform. When her man is away she is bound by custom to visit him whenever prison rules and regulations permit her to do so. She is his link with the outside world, a carrier of messages, a smuggler of prohibited articles and last, but by no means least, a source of comfort even though she may normally only see her spouse through a reinforced glass screen.

It's a life where everything is centred on the man in prison during the time he's away. Letters have to be written containing, with an eye on the censor, only news which will pass his eagle inspection. If the prisoner has a record of attempted escapes communication becomes even more tricky. An innocent reference to some event in the family might be taken as a coded instruction. In such cases the letter does not reach its proper destination and the wife is in for some stick on her next visit. By and large she is normally on to a hiding for nothing.

When her man is out the wife plays no part in his social life. When he and his colleagues pull off a nice tickle they will celebrate at some club or other. The wives are definitely out of the picture at these jollifications, and it's a fair bet that any females present are of the obliging variety, a fact well-known to the wives, who have no option but to swallow it.

That lark is now over and done with.

It's a great relief to know that, when a knock comes on the door, it's only the postman or a friendly visitor.

Ellen Cannon.

CHAPTER ONE

JOE:

I have often thought about how it was that I became "dangerous", a hard man with a ready pair of fists and a shooter tucked into his belt. It's true that I was born and brought up in Notting Dale, which has more villains to the square mile than any other manor in London, but that's not the explanation. After all, among my school-mates were some famous names in the sports field John Murray, ex-Middlesex and ex England cricketer, ex-Footballer's, Alan Mullery, and Jimmy Bloomfield. There were many more who rose from their slum beginnings to carve out respectable lives. So where did I go wrong ?

I've come to the conclusion that I was simply born rotten just as surely as if I'd been given a stocking mask and a sawn-off shotgun as christening presents. My early environment didn't mould my character. Had I lived in the posh district of Holland Park I would have turned out to be a cad and a bounder. As it was, Notting Dale supplied the accent and the education (or lack of it) and I was on my way to becoming a thief and a villain.

Notting Dale lies adjacent to Notting Hill, which is at the arsehole end of the Bayswater Road. The Council flat Morland house, in Lancaster Road, where I was born was so small we had to move to Princedale Road. It was an old house which had gone to rack and ruin. The family daily risked life and limb as they trod the decaying stairway and rotten floorboards. I was still only a babe-in-arms, so Ma had to watch her step when she was carrying me around.

I was three years old when the second World War broke out. It coincided with the family removing to a new home in Avondale Park Gardens, which was altogether more suitable for our large family. There was a yard at the rear and a large open space at the front where the kids could play in fine weather. At a later stage in the war the Council provided us with a bonus in the shape of a large iron-framed cage which was erected in the front room and was designed to protect us in case the house fell down. The younger end of the family made full use of it as an Aladdin's cave, a pirate den or a refuge from parental anger.

An area which attracted our childish curiosity was the underground shelter which had been constructed in the middle of the large open space in front of the houses. It was intended to provide an alternative to being flattened inside a metal cage. Mum didn't go a lot on either of these safeguards, vowing that no bleeding Hitler was going to send her down holes in the ground when she had her washing and mending and God knows what else to do. Yet every time the air-raid warning sounded she would gather us kids around her and shepherd us down the shelter.

The war had been going on for a couple of years when the time came for me to begin my schooling. I must say I didn't go a bundle on the State's efforts to prepare me for a useful life as a responsible member of society. In my childish eyes the teachers were a terrifying bunch of ogres, handing out clips round the earhole and sketchy instruction in the three R's (Reading, Riting and Rithmetic) in approximately equal proportions. I didn't care much for the discipline either, and as a result spent more time roaming the streets with my mates than I spent in the classroom. We called it "playing the wag"; going to school in the morning, getting marked in and then disappearing for the rest of the day. There was plenty to occupy our time. High on the list of out-of-school activities was dodging the School Board inspector, who roamed the streets looking for truants. He had no chance really. Hunting a mob of fleet-footed kids who knew every alley and side-street like the palms of their hands was no job for a middle-aged geezer with a C3 Army medical rating.

Some afternoons would be spent at the local cinema. The Royalty in Lancaster Road or the Bug-hole in the Portobello Road Market. We clubbed together for one of us to pay for admission. The lucky one would choose a suitable moment, usually the fortissimo part of a cowboy picture, to open one of the emergency exits and let the rest in. Once we were inside the ushers were no problem, since they were elderly men or women who had no wish to tangle with a gang of tough kids.

On hot summer days the temptation to go swimming was almost irresistible, but it was out of the question. The baths in Lancaster Road also housed the public washing facilities which were regularly used by our mothers. Apart from this, a further deterrent was the daily presence of a female dragon known as Nitty Norah, the champion de-louser of Notting Dale.

This lady had the most unappetising job you could imagine. Groups of kids, about twenty or thirty at a time, were marched to the baths from the local schools. The not-too-tender hands of Nitty Norah rubbed a foul-smelling fluid into their scalps, after which a fine-toothed metal comb was painfully raked through the wet locks. Norah would collect a fine haul of lice which she surveyed with the same sort of pride as a Scottish laird would regard the bag after a good shoot.

7

There were compensations in my life at school which went a long way towards making it tolerable. On the days when physical training was on the curriculum, Cannon J.D. was always among those present. The reason was that boxing instruction was part of the programme, and I had discovered in myself a talent in, and a liking for, the noble art of self-defence. This was not surprising. My father had been a well-known bare-knuckle fighter, my brother Bill was a promising ama-teur who was later to turn pro, my uncle Jim was a boxing referee and my other brothers were very handy with their dukes. At St. Francis', my first school, I began to learn the rudiments, with a little help from Dad, who used the backyard as a training ground.

It was in the nature of things that I should be expelled from St. Francis', whose Headmaster expressed the opinion that a zoo would be a more fitting place for my further education. I didn't go to a zoo, but to another school on the manor; the law insisted, my parents had to agree or be prosecuted, so I enroled at St. Johns'. This place was very similar to St. Francis', and I hated it just as much. My life became a constant battle against authority, a situation which was not made any better by the fact that my home was within a stone's throw of the nick in Sirdar Road, one of the two stations in B Divi-sion of the Metropolitan Police. The other station was a Victorian building at the corner of Ladbroke Road and Ladbroke Grove, not far from Holland Park tube. I was to become intimately acquainted with the interiors of both these places, but that lay in the future. At the time I was aware of the proximity of the Old Bill, which hampered my activities to some extent.

Shortly after my ninth birthday the war in Europe ended. I was now an accomplished little tea-leaf, a pint-sized terror who couldn't be left alone with anything of value unless it was nailed down. Even then I would find some way of capturing it. I'd been at it for a long time, nicking lead from bombed buildings, for which there was a ready sale and no questions asked, and either alone or mob-handed making raids on the local shops.

I was only caught once. I teamed up with a kid called Jeff Lucas to do some of the shops in the area. The way we worked was that one of us would distract the attention of the shopkeeper while the other crept in below counter-level and nicked whatever was handy. We would then share out the loot in a nearby air-raid shelter which we used as headquarters. The scheme was a huge success until one day, as we sat in the shelter gorging ourselves on sherbet dips and toffees, we were surprised by one of our shopkeeper victims along with our respective fathers.

There was no chance of putting in a decent plea as our mouths were full of the evidence, nor did the situation lend itself to peaceful discussion. My old man took off his belt and gave me a good thrashing, Jeff's father performed likewise with his son, and there the matter ended.

It was round about that time that I collected my first black eye. I was very much king of the kids on my manor with a reputation as a battler so I didn't take kindly to anyone who questioned my authority. I got into an argument with one of the local girls, a right tomboy who ran around with the boys, played football with them and was the first Women's Libber in my experience. She slung me a right-hander which made me see stars. I was so shocked that I forgot to hit her back.

By the evening, when I arrived home, the eye had developed into a real beauty, a classic shiner which spread the colours of the rainbow over half my face.

Naturally my old man wanted to know how I had come by this spectacular disfigurement, so I went into a song-and-dance about an attack by a gang of kids from the Portobello Road. My sister Doreen put the kybosh on that little romance. 'It was Joanie Farmer did it, Dad,' she said. 'I saw her.' I had to take a lot of stick from the family over that caper.

My brother Billy was very scornful. 'Fancy letting yourself get belted by a judy,' he said, and carted me off to the Rugby Club in Walmer Road, where he handed me over to John Croxton, with instructions to give me some special coaching in self-defence 'in case I was attacked by any more girls'.

The Rugby Club was a new experience. It's full title was the Rugby School Club. It had been started some years previously by the boys of Rugby public school as part of their social service work. The idea behind the project was to get poor kids off the streets and into an environment where they could be given every encouragement to become useful citizens. The warden was a chap called Jim Lane, a dedicated youth worker.

I enroled as a member of the club and turned up more or less regularly for three years. The main attraction of the place for me was the excellent boxing instruction, of which I took full advantage. In the inter-club contests in the London Federation of Boys' Clubs I picked up a few cups and medals in my weight class which was, believe it or not, five stones and one and a half pounds!

One of my medals gave me particular pride. It was presented to me in 1948 by the Duke of Edinburgh when our boxing team defeated teams from Canterbury, Oxford and Bermondsey.

My boxing skills improved as a result of my association with the club but I can't say the same for my character. St. Johns' school saw less and less of me, which didn't seem to bother them unduly, and I spent a lot of time at the local markets helping the barrow boys and earning a few bob. Yet the most fruitful source of income lay in the derelict buildings and their rich store of lead and zinc.

Unfortunately there's always a fly in the ointment. My particular fly was the Old Bill who, now that the war was over, were able to devote more time to the prevention of felony which was a way of life for most of the population of Notting Dale. I missed many a good tickle because of their increased watchfulness. Their suspicions were quite naturally aroused by the sight of a ragged-arsed nipper carrying a heavy sack through the streets en route to the nearest scrapyard. As a consequence I was obliged to find other targets for my thieving.

Such targets were not hard to discover. Notting Dale was a poor area where the residents showed no great eagerness to pay their bills. On the other side of the picture were the gas and electricity undertakings whose public service did not include the provision of free lighting and heating. Hence, every house in the district was equipped with pre-payment meters whose coin-boxes yielded a rich harvest of bobs and pennies to the enterprising thief.

The *modus operandum* was simple. The front doors of the houses were furnished with Yale locks, but the majority of the inhabitants saw no reason to spend good money on duplicate keys when a single key suspended from a length of string through the letter box served the same purpose. So it was just a matter of fishing out the key, nipping inside, forcing the fragile locks on the coin-boxes and clearing out the contents.

Another caper which paid dividends was the sell-back. I would climb over the fence at the rear of a scrapyard, sort out some portable gear and then take it round the front and sell it to the dealer, who had no idea that he was buying his own property. After all, one piece of lead pipe looks very much like another. Percy Horn, the largest scrap metal dealer on the manor, was a frequent victim. He still managed to make a fortune.

The end result of my thieving was that I always had ample supplies of cash money. My greatest problem was concealing it from the family, for in our house there was little privacy. luckily my old man was out all day on his job as a meter inspector, which he had held for thirty years, and my Mum worked mornings as an office cleaner. My brothers and sisters, however, were in and out of the house at all hours. To lessen the risk of discovery I used more than one hiding place for my ill-gotten gains.

The bedroom which I shared with my brothers was my first choice as a safe deposit. I levered up a floor-board in one corner of the room and slipped a roll of notes into the cavity. My second choice was the loft at the top of the house, which was full of old furniture and the discarded bric-a-brac of a large family. There were so many hidey-holes here that I could take my pick, which I did, varying the locations from time to time. The bulk of the money I stuffed into a cocoa tin with a close-fitting lid, which I buried in the back garden.

It was just as well that I took the precaution of dividing the loot, because one day my Mum decided to give the bedroom a turn-out. She noticed the loose floorboard, took a look under it and found the wages. When I came in that evening my father was sitting in the living room with the evidence spread out on the table in front of him.

'What's this, Joey,' he said as I walked in the door.

'Dunno, Dad,' I said. My confession of ignorance

earned me a clip round the ear.

'It's money, you thieving little bleeder,' he said.

'Where did you get it?'

I turned on the waterworks. There's nothing like a few tears for softening a parent's heart.

'I don't know nothing about it, Dad,' I sobbed. 'It don't belong to me'.

I stuck to my story. Dad questioned my brother Peter, who also knew nothing. I learned then my first lesson in law, that suspicion is one thing but proof is another. I don't know what happened to the money, but I reckon that Mum copped for the lot, because the table was that much richer for a few days. In a way I was rather proud to contribute to the family budget even in a roundabout way. As for the loss of the cash, it didn't mean a thing. There was plenty more in the loft and the garden, so I didn't go short.

Looking back over my life, I can honestly say that I've never been really concerned over money, principally I suppose because I've always had enough of that commodity, and I think I can say truthfully that neither greed nor penury drove me to crime. As to my violent tendencies, when I was boxing as a kid I was not content to obey the rules. When the bell went I was conscious only of a desire to destroy the other fellow, to beat him into the ground. It was a feeling in me over which I had no control, and it was the same when I grew up. If it was me or the other chap for it, then he had to lose.

I was hooked on boxing at a very early age, influenced to a large extent by my elder brothers; Billy did his training in a makeshift gym behind a barber's shop in Princedale Road. I often went along to see him work out. It was magic. I can still smell the sharp odour of embrocation and stale sweat which contrasted oddly with the perfumes drifting in from the barber's, and I retain vivid mental pictures of the gloved gladiators knocking hell out of each other, grunting and groaning and scuffling their feet on the resined canvas.

I watched points carefully, because I had my eyes set on a career as a professional fighter. I soon caught on to the fact that a pro is not inhibited by sticking too close to the Queensberry rules. My brother Billy fought in boxing booths and local venues where the refereeing was not too strict and the audience bayed for blood. He knew all the tricks of the business, pulling an opponent on to the punch, treading on the toes, going in with the shoulder under the chin, popping the thumb in the eye and so on. I began to use these tactics at the Rugby Club, and soon became known as a dirty fighter, which didn't bother me at all so long as I came out on top.

On one occasion I came across a kid who knew as much about the dirty trick end of the business as I did. We mauled each other for a couple of rounds, but in the third I got fed up and steamed in with my head down, butting the other kid in the face. The instructor stopped the bout on the spot and gave me a rucking, which did no damage to my pride. It didn't mend my opponent's broken hooter either.

Sometimes I would go along with Billy to Lime Grove, a well-known venue which had seen the debut of many a budding champion. Alf Mancini of the famous boxing family handled most of the promotions there. My uncle Jim was on the panel of referees. Lime Grove was only a couple of miles down the road from Notting Dale, and whenever Billy was performing he pulled a good crowd from the fight fans on the manor.

The events at Lime Grove were conducted according to the rules of the British Boxing Board of Control, and all the fighters and their managers were licensed, so I had no chance of slipping into Billy's corner as sponge man, a job I had often done in less proper surroundings. All the same I got as close to the ring as possible and shouted and yelled advice to the fighters. At times like these I felt I was really living.

There were some odd characters knocking around the Dale when I was a kid, old lags who remembered the days when the Old Bill never ventured into Bangor Street after dark, eccentrics of all shapes, sizes and sexes who found the lure of the Portobello Road irresistible, and many others who lent colour to the surroundings.

Father George Long was a character who came to the Dale just after the end of the war. He was anything but the conventional Roman Catholic priest. In fact in his biography (A!l I could never be, published by Leslie Frewin in 1966) he confessed that he was not cut out for the job. He was a great sportsman, mad keen on cricket and boxing, and one of his first acts was to start a boys' club, using the premises of St, Francis' school in the evenings.

He was very friendly with my brother Nobby and they often came back to our house together for a bite to eat after an evening at one of the local pubs. All the family liked him, probably because he didn't put on any airs and graces. On one of these visits he had a few words with me, asking me what I wanted to be when I grew up. I think it shook him when I said I was going to he the toughest of the tough.

One of the reasons he found favour with the residents of the Dale was because he had plenty of bottle. When it came to it he wasn't afraid of having a go, as was proved when a certain firm connected with Billy Hill came to the Warwick Castle looking for Ginger Randall There had been some aggro at Sandown Park races and Ginger was marked down for a bit of treatment.

The Warwick Castle was owned by Ruby Sparks, a notorious ex-jewel thief who had once made a well-publicised escape from Dartmoor. The pub was patronised almost exclusively by the villains of the Dale, and Ginger had considerable support among them. On this particular night some of the hounds were all tooled-up in readiness for a full-scale battle.

Someone had tipped off the Reverend Father, and when the firm came on the scene he was standing at the bar waiting for them. What he said nobody knew, though many garbled reports were circulated later, but it ended with the firm marching out of the pub without seeing to Ginger Randall or anyone else. It transpired that the whole thing would have fizzled out in any event, but Father Long wasn't to know that when he fronted the gang.

I was on to my third school, Addison Road Secondary Modern which, unlike St Francis' and St, John's, was co-educational. I wasn't much into the girl scene, regarding them as inferior beings fit only for an occasional groping in some quiet doorway or fumbling attacks on their virtue in the dark privacy of a bombed building. Not that the female presence at Addison drove me to play the wag increasingly. I was a natural-born truant.

From the academic point of view I wasn't all that bright. Indeed, at the age of fourteen my handwriting was deplorable, I could do simple addition and subtraction and the sum total of my knowledge in other subjects could be written in large letters on the back of a postage stamp. Nevertheless, I could estimate to a penny the value of a lump of lead piping and I knew at any time the exact value of the sums hidden in my various safe deposits.

In spite of what was an excellent cash flow situation,

a source of constant irritation was that I could not spend my money on such obvious adornments as clothes and jewellery. While some of my older mates strutted about in the latest fashions, I had to be content with cast-offs from my brothers, jerseys with holes in the elbows, ragged trousers with patches in the arse and shoes which had been cobbled so often that very little of the original leather was left. I only had one consolation. I was able to indulge my appetite for sweets and purchase the loyalty of other kids with showers of bullseyes, peppermint chocs, hundreds and thousands, gob-stoppers, jelly babies and the like.

Inevitably the day came when I was caught bang to rights on a bomb site with a pile of lead neatly packed and ready to be carried away, I appeared before a juvenile court by way of the nick in Sirdar Road and copped for twelve month's probation, which didn't hurt as much as the belting my old man gave me. Probation was a bind. I had to report to the probation officer once a week and he kept in close touch with my school, which limited my activities to a great extent, I didn't feel any social stigma, because most of the other kids on the manor were in the same boat.

The most important by-product of my trouble with the Old Bill was the effect on my finances. My card was marked at the local nick and the coppers on the beat knew me by sight, so I had to be extra careful. With no money coming in and quite a bit going out to support my life-style, it wasn't long before I was down to my last couple of pounds, I decided to try my luck in the neighbouring manor of Paddington where I wasn't known.

Opening up new fields may work well in some businesses, It didn't work in mine, In the Dale I was among friends. Paddington was alien territory where I was on my own against some tough competition. It wasn't long before I was nicked, and this time the juvenile court wasn't so lenient, They decided that what was needed to bring me back on the straight and narrow was a spell at an attendance centre, which is how I came to be introduced to Peel House,

The attendance centre scheme for young offenders was a Home Office idea designed in theory to rehabilitate teenage criminals through work and discipline, What happened in practice was that I reported to Peel House every week and spent a couple of hours scrubbing floors under the casual supervision of a staff who couldn't have cared less what we did so long as they collected their wages.

I was now a fully paid up member of the Juvenile Crime Club and as such had a certain status in the Dale. The young kids looked up to me as a professional while my equals, fellow floor-scrubbers, tried to rope me in on any villainy that was afoot. In the result I was as surely a candidate for Borstal as if I had had my name put down at birth.

It was a relief when I was able to opt out of the State educational system and leave Addison Road Secondary Modern. I was given a written reference by the headmaster, in which he did his best to conceal his opinion of me under a mass of flowery prose. With a fixed determination to avoid any form of work which did not return high wages for the least possible effort, I fell into screwing (not the sexual variety) and, under the expert tuition of my seniors, soon became highly skilled in the art of breaking and entering.

For a time everything in the garden was lovely. I kidded my Mum and Dad that I was working on the barrows, made regular contributions to the family budget and was thus in a position to indulge in the luxury of new clothes in place of the hand-me-downs that I had been obliged to wear. I went screwing practically every night, either alone or with one of my pals, and was so successful that I began to believe that I had a charmed life. I swaggered around the Dale in my new gear, spending money as though it came out of a tap and, as I now see clearly, attracting the attention of the Old Bill, who had me marked down for treatment when the opportunity arose.

They had their chance before long. I set out one night to do a snouter's in Shepherd's Bush, wearing the proper gear of dark sweater and trousers, rubber-soled shoes and black gloves. What I didn't know as I flitted through the back streets was that I was being followed by a pair of CID men.

I went in about eleven o'clock. The door was a doddle and, since I had cased the joint thoroughly, I knew exactly where to put my hands on the cash. I had it in my pocket, about a couple of hundred in notes, when the Old Bill jumped me and I was caught bang to rights.

This would have been an ordinary nicking but for one important difference. I was carrying a .22 Browning automatic tucked into the waistband of my trousers, a foolish touch of bravado which was totally unnecessary. I had bought the weapon for a few quid from a kid who had nicked it from his elder brother. There had been a full clip in the gun when I got it, but I had fired off four rounds in a quiet part of Wormwood Scrubs, a large open space adjoining the prison.

When the Old Bill came across the shooter in the course of giving me a rub-down, it was like a scene from the Sweeney. The detective constable extracted the gun and held it out for inspection by the detective sergeant.

We've got a real desperate villain here, Sarge,' he

said.

The DS took the shooter and slipped out the clip. He had handled guns before, and he made that obvious.

'One up the spout, eh? All ready to shoot some poor innocent citizen. This should get you about ten years, chummy,' he said.

I kept my mouth shut. There wasn't much point in saying anything. When they got me into the nick they gave me a lot of verbal, suggesting that I made things easier, for myself by confessing to various unsolved burglaries. I didn't fall for that one. I knew I was for the high jump, so the least said soonest mended.

In due course I appeared before Stamford House Juvenile Court, where they were beginning to know my face. They didn't exactly welcome me with open arms as an old member of the club. I was committed to an Approved School where, so the authorities thought, I would see the error of my ways and have my feet set in the paths of righteousness.

I remember the date well. It was the 16th of October,1952.

There were a lot of kids I knew to whom home was only another four-letter word, whose parents didn't give a monkey's for them and who didn't feel deprived when they were taken into care or otherwise disposed of. It wasn't like that in my family, for we were very close to each other, with strong emotional ties, Now, for the first time in my life, I couldn't go home to my Mum and Dad or the rest of the family because I was locked up and likely to be in that situation for some time.

That wasn't the worst of it. For a couple of years I had been going steady with a girl called Ellen Proctor. She was about the same age as me whose birthday was the same day as my Mother's. She was also a member of a large family who were well respected in the Dale. She was a very good-looking girl and was later to become my wife and the mother of our two children, but that's in the future. For the present it looked as though I was going to be deprived of a relationship that had become an important part of my life. I thought of myself as a tough kid, but even the toughest have their romantic feelings, and I was in love with Ellen and she was in love with me. In my heart of hearts I knew that, whatever the future held in store, she would be there waiting for me. Missing her played a large part in my planning to have it away from the Approved School at the earliest opportunity.

I was detained at Stamford House overnight. On the following morning I was told that I would be held for classification before being sent to the grade of Approved School which could safely be entrusted with the person of one J.D.Cannon, youthful desperado and menace to society. Having been nicked in possession of a loaded shooter, it was a safe bet that I wasn't down for transfer to a convalescent home.

My destination would be a place where they were long on discipline and security and short on home comforts.

The authorities didn't seem to be in much of a hurry to decide my fate. On the other hand, I was determined to be out of Stamford House as soon as possible. To an expert, which is how I thought of myself, breaking out of a gaff presents roughly the same problem as breaking in. I gathered a half-dozen kids together and led a mass escape to freedom over the back gate. There's not only safety in numbers but helpful confusion as well. Needless to say we were all recaptured pretty quickly, but I did get as far as the Dale and a meeting with Ellen before I was picked up.

The rest of my stay at Stamford House was short, but I didn't lack attention. To judge by the way the staff kept watch on me they must have considered that I was a valuable commodity, and even when Mum and Dad came to visit me they didn't relax their vigilance. Father Long made an appearance and did his best to convince me that what had happened wasn't the end of the world. I couldn't agree with him, but at least he tried.

The authorities finally made up their minds that St. Christopher's Approved School in Hayes was a suitable place for my further education, a prospect which was as welcome to me as a third nostril. Having spent years playing the wag from St. Francis and St. John, I was now to be locked in the bosom of St. Christopher, the patron saint of travellers. Maybe it was an omen, for I definitely intended to travel as far as I could in a direction away from that seat of learning.

St. Christopher's was a large country house standing in its own grounds in the suburb of Hayes about ten miles from the centre of London. From the outside it looked like a public school, but there the similarity ended. All the windows were securely screwed up and there were locks and bolts everywhere. The inmates wore a uniform of sorts, short cord trousers and a battledress-style jacket, which gave no sense of pride to the wearer and was definitely no joy to behold.

The kids were accommodated in dormitories, each containing as many beds as could be crammed into the available space.

During the night hours attempted buggery and other forms of sexual assault were common, but I was not one of the victims. I knocked seven shades of shit out of the first lad to try it on with me.

My reputation as an escapee had followed me from

Stamford House, so I had to watch points for a few weeks. I was a good boy went quietly about my work and caused no trouble, then one niqht I took the screws out of one of the dormitory windows, using a screwdriver that I had nicked from the metalwork class, and had it away. One of the kids put the screws back and my absence was not discovered until the following morning, by which time I was enjoying the hospitality of one of my married sisters in the Dale.

My period of liberty lasted ten days, which I put to good use. I screwed a few gaffs and blued the proceeds on evenings out with Ellen, but in due course I was nicked and it was back to St. Christopher's. They were a forgiving lot. I got a touch of the cane, which only acted as a spur for I was out again the same day. The festive season was only a few days off, and I was set on enjoying Christmas in my own way.

I was more careful this time. I stayed away from my usual haunts had a good Christmas, a riotous New Year, and was in fact free until the middle of April when I was picked up in Paddington by an eagle-eyed PC. Back at St, Christopher's they offered to waive the caning routine if I would give my word that I wouldn't try another escape. I chose to take the punishment without mortgaging my future, and sure enough I was away again within a couple of days,

My unofficial leave lasted almost two months, and might have lasted longer had I resisted the temptation to make one in a store break which was a non-starter from the off. I should have known better than to go to work with a couple of riqht amateurs with a lot of rabbit and no bottle. We got into the gaff with no trouble, which wasn't surprising because as soon as we were inside the lights went on and the Old Bill was waiting for us mob-handed.

That episode marked the end of my on-off relationship with St. Christopher, I had chanced my arm once too often. On the 9th of June 1953, at the County of London Sessions, I was sentenced to Borstal.

CHAPTER TWO

ELLEN:

From what I've heard and read the public idea of a villain's wife is a brassy blonde with rings all over her fingers, dressed up to the nines in very bad taste, enjoying the good life when her man is doing the business and living in the lap of luxury when he is paying the penalty for his crimes in one or other of Her Majesty's prisons.

This is a load of old rubbish. The truth is that a villain's woman is just as much on the crime scene as her man. She has no option. She has to lie for him, cover for him, sometimes hide the proceeds of his villainy, take care of the kids when he's inside and learn how to keep her mouth shut when it comes on top.

I've been mixed up with criminals almost the whole of my life. To start with I was born and bred in a London district that has always had more than its fair share of thieves and villains. In my childhood they were pointed out to me. Oh, there goes so-and-so. He was in on that bank job, got away with twenty grand, copped for seven years. Nobody thought any the worse of him for that. My father was always in and out of prison, but even so he managed to spare enough time to keep my mother in an almost constant state of pregnancy. As a consequence we were a large family. I was the eldest.

In Notting Dale there were many families similar to mine. Some were respectable, some weren't, but nobody looked down on jailbirds. They were held to be 'unlucky' to have fallen foul of the law, because in one way or another the inhabitants of the Dale regarded the police as a natural enemy. There were areas where the Old Bill never ventured alone. always in pairs. They fought an uphill battle. They nicked thieves and put them away, but they couldn't cure the poverty that drove men to break the law. The thieves continued thieving, their respectable friends bought the proceeds at knock-down prices and everybody was happy - except the Old Bill.

Little girls never remained little for long in the Dale. They matured very early. To them the facts of life were facts and not fiction. Families lived on top of each other in the slums and children slept in the same room as their parents who made no secret of what they were up to as they coupled. Out on the streets it was a jungle where perverts enticed small girls into dark corners and subjected them to all sorts of sexual abuse. Nothing like that happened to me. It would be a very brave nonce who would try it on with Charlie Proctor's little girl and I was under the protection of friends and relatives who were quite capable of inflicting grievous bodily harm. In a tough neighbourhood you had to be tough to survive. You couldn't afford to be sentimental either.

I don't want to give the impression that I was a goody-goody. I was curious about sex and I knew what some of the girls my own age got up to with the boys. It was a constant topic of conversation. One of my best friends told me that she had lost her virginity at the age of twelve. She boasted that she had had more dick than I'd had good dinners and ended by saying that she loved it and couldn't get enough. I felt sorry for her. My memories of my childhood are confused. The war broke out when I was two years old and it was all very strange to me. When the bombing of London started with air raid sirens going off and houses being blown up I remember I was scared to death.

At the time I didn't understand what was happening and why, but looking back I think tha things like these left their mark on very young children. Violent death is not a pretty sight when seen through the eyes of an infant or those of an adult for that matter. Anyway, time passed, the war was over and the residents of the Dale got back to normal living in so far as the continuation of rationing permitted. In that area we did very well. We were never short of food and there was more black market grub in our house than there was in the shops. My dad was forever turning up with carrier bags stuffed with all kinds of goodies. Where they came from I didn't know and I didn't ask.

I think I was my dad's favourite of all the family, because when he was at home he took me with him almost everywhere. If he had a bit of business on he would leave me at Carrie Mancini's caff in Bramley Road. Carrie was married to Joe Mancini, the brother of Alf Mancini who was a well-known boxer. Another place I got to know well was Stump Chamberlain's yard on the corner of Poynton Street opposite the Duke of Sussex pub. He sold statues and garden ornaments. I used to play there till my dad came and picked me up. He always smelled strongly of drink, but I was used to that. I think the only time he was really sober was when he was asleep in bed.

I was lucky that the war didn't interfere much with my schooling. I started at Sirdar Road Infants when I was about five. There wasn't much in the way of education going on there due to shortage of teachers. It was better after the end of the war when I went to Saunder's Grove Junior school, where I did quite well. The next step was the Senior school at Sirdar Road, and I finally ended up at Wendell Park Senior, which I left when I was fourteen. There was a little bunch of us who went through the various schools together. There was Margaret Hunter, Jean Bruce, Jean Coleman and Rosie Rust who are all now married and with families of their own.

Talking about families, familiar names were always cropping up in the Dale. My own lot, the Proctors, were well known. So were the Cannons, another large family who had fingers in many pies. One of them was Joe Cannon, a boy of about my own age, who I later married. Then there were the Suttons, the Careys, Worleys, Bernard, Beadles, Mitchells, Murphys, Stanleys, Oatways, Varys, Wises and Birches. One way or another they were all related. I don't know if marriage between cousins was legal but in Notting Dale they made their own laws. The result was the families had ties of blood as well as marriage, which brought them closer together. They all knew each other's business and if you kicked one of them they all limped.

Crescent Street, where I was born, was one of the most notorious streets in London. There was violence there, but there was great loyalty. In a way it was a very happy place to live in. In spite of overcrowding and poverty there was lots of laughter.

Looking back at myself as a teenage school leaver I see a quite handsome girl and, though I say it without intending to boast, a person with above average intelligence. I had benefited from such education as the State provided, but there was no hope in those days of further education. It was finish school at fourteen and out to work. Thankfully in the early fifties there were jobs to go to, most of them menial but that didn't bother me. There were opportunities to attend evening classes and I took advantage of them to study book-keeping and managed to get a qualification which came in very useful in later years. Mathematics and English had been my best subjects at school. I looked forward to making some sort of a mark in life. After all there were many success stories of kids from the Dale making good in spite of the handicaps. One of them was Jimmy Gregory who lived in the same block of flats as the Cannons in Lancaster Road and ended up owning Queens Park Rangers football club. Also there was Fred Enniss, a close friend of the Cannons, who became Mayor of Hammersmith. His wife, Poppy, was born and bred in the Dale. She was a Bedworth, and her mother owned flower stalls in Norland Market and Portobello Road.

Now that I was going out to work and earning money I felt more independent. Joe Cannon and I had been mixed up with each other for a long time, and we'd gone through the usual stages, playing mothers and fathers and doctors and nurses. The time had to come for the real thing and, as soon as a suitable opportunity turned up, we did it. It wasn't the Barbara Cartland stuff, just a slightly painful experience, but from then on I was Joe's girl. He had just left school and divided his time between casual jobs in the market and going out with his mates on screwing expeditions. He was never short of money and he spent quite a lot on me.

It was about this time that my dad landed in real bother. He was driving a lorry in the Harrow Road which was loaded with timber and in the cab with him were his brother-in-law Dick Lambert and a woman called Cotton. It was late at night and the three of them had been on the booze most of the day. Now my dad was known as a skilful driver but his luck was out that night. He ran down two women and killed them and drove on.

He was duly nicked and committed for trial at the Old Bailey, where he was sent down for three years and disqualified for ten years. This was a blow for the family, but it was not unexpected, because it had to happen one day. Like others in the Dale we accepted the situation. Three years, with time off for good behaviour, wasn't a lifetime. I remember I felt sorry for the two women who had been killed but most of my sorrow was for my mum. As was the habit in the Dale our friends rallied round and helped where they could.

They say that troubles never come singly. My Joe was on probation after having been nicked for a bit of thieving. His position was not out of the way. Most of the kids in the Dale were in the same boat and there was no shame attached to it. As for Joe, he just continued thieving and nothing could be done about that either. There was one thing that troubled me, and that was when he began to mess about with guns, but I knew better than to argue with him about it. He had a way of looking at you if he was crossed that put an end to the conversation. To him probation was a joke, something to be taken in his stride.

He didn't seem to be bothered when he was nicked on one of his screwing expeditions, but he was carrying a gun and that bothered the law. They had him into an approved school sharpish, but that didn't faze him. He was out of there and on the trot in no time at all. The first thing he did was to get in touch with me, which wasn't very wise of him because the law was watching out. He learned his lesson very quickly and on his next escape he kept away from the Dale. He got messages to me and we would meet on another manor. He still carried on with his law-breaking antics, so inevitably came the day when he was caught bang to rights. This time the punishment was Borstal which would put him out of circulation for some considerable time.

I have got to say at this point that I had the support of all the Cannon family. My Joe's brothers, especially Nobby, Tommy and George kept an eye on me and I spent more time in the Cannon family home than I spent in my own. Joe's mum was a diamond. She understood what I was going through, what with my dad being away and all that, and she was like a second mother to me. My aunt Kit also gave me a lot of encouragement. I remember her saying to me that I should stick by my Joe no matter what people might say about him. She was a very wise old lady who had gone through a lot in her time and I listened to her.

So the days and weeks and months rolled by. Joe wasn't a great letter-writer but I heard from him that, although Borstal wasn't a holiday camp, he was managing to get by, so I just sat and waited for him to come home.

CHAPTER THREE

JOE:

My first step on the road to Borstal was a few weeks in the young prisoners wing of Wormwood Scrubs prison. This was my first taste of bird, and I didn't go for it all that much. The screws put themselves about and went in for a lot of shouting and hollering, which scared the living daylights out of most of the kids. It didn't frighten me.

I had my first introduction to the system of 'slopping out', a degrading and disgusting experience which took place in the early hours of the morning when we were unlocked. It consisted of a line of kids carrying their pisspots to be emptied in the single recess on each landing. These pots contained the filth accumulated during the night, urine, spew, turds of shit and spittle, all to be disposed of in double quick time. The last in line waded ankle-deep in piss and shit. I thought to myself then, as I have often thought since, that even animals are not subject to such horrifying treatment. If the RSPCA ever get into the Scrubs, they'll close the place down.

I had just about had a bellyfull of this performance when I was told that I had been allocated to Portland Borstal near Weymouth. There was a dozen of us all told, and we went by coach under the watchful eyes of a couple of screws. It was a fine August day, the sun was shining brilliantly and, as the coach bowled along at the start of the four hour journey, we were all in fairly good spirits. A few kids burst into song, but the screws soon put a stop to that.

I had never in my life been farther away from London than the hopfields of Kent where most of the poorer families from the Dale spent the month of September each year. We travelled by horse and cart or packed into a lorry laden with bedding chairs, tables and household goods. Our homes were a collection of corrugated, iron huts, our beds straw palliasses laid on wooden frames. Starting at seven o'clock in the morning, the families picked hops all day and in the evenings, while the parents went on the piss in the local pubs, the kids would play games around the shanties. Some of the older ones paired off and went into the fields for sex sessions, which led to the usual crop of shot-gun weddings the following spring.

Portland when we finally arrived, turned out to be a grim, semi-fortified group of buildings perched on a rocky island site which was joined to the mainland by a long causeway. I kept my eyes open when we got there, and reckoned the chances of escape from this drum would be nil. It must have been the windiest part of the British Isles. There was a rope strung permanently between the kitchen quarters and the main building, but even with the aid of this device the crossing was a struggle against the elements. That we got our food on time was a daily miracle.

The Borstal was divided into 'houses', a sort of public school idea which was intended, I suppose, to encourage good-natured rivalry. The rivalry was there alright, but it wasn't very friendly. As I remember there was Drake House, Benbow House, and there must have been other naval heroes whose names were commemorated. I found myself in Raleigh~ a name that meant nothing to me except that I had often nicked bicycles of that description.

I soon settled in to the routine. We were made to work

hard, but there were some compensations. One of the screws was a former professional boxer by the name of Vince Hawkins, who spotted that I had the makings of a fighter and gave me some personal coaching. It's a funny thing that there were no classes in safe-cracking or breaking and entering, but plenty of opportunity to learn how to punch peoples' heads in. I went for that. Nothing ensures respect and a trouble-free passage through Borstal than the ability to hammer a fellow inmate into insensibility.

It was quite by accident that I became the Borstal barber. I had never handled a pair of scissors before, but that didn't seem to matter. After a ten minute course of instruction from one of the screws I was let loose to do my worst, and some of it was pretty horrible. However I soon got the hang of it, Some of the lads were quite proud of their barnets, and a bit of care on my part was rewarded with a gift of snout, which I was able to exchange for sweets or other goodies, Just the same, though I made a few friends I also made a lot of enemies. That was where my fighting ability came in useful.

They were a mixed bunch at Portland, drawn from all parts of the British Isles. There were the Cockneys from London the Jocks from Scotland and the Taffs from Wales, The Liverpool lot were known as Scouses. Then there were the Brummies from Birmingham with accents so thick that it was hard to understand them.

It was natural for cliques to form. Each little mob thought they were the business and the rest were idiots, The Scousses were the worst. They were an evil bunch who never lost an opportunity to cause a row, One day they picked on a Cockney kid and gave him a proper seeing-to which led to a punch-up between Scouses and Cockneys. I was in the thick of it from the start, and copped for one of the hard cases, He opened proceedings by grabbing me by the lapels of my jacket and butting me in the face. I heard the bone crack, the claret flowed and for a moment I was blinded by the pain, Then I went berserk. Putting a knee into his cobblers, I gave him a couple of hooks as he went down and then kicked the shit out of him.

The fight was broken up by the screws and the injured were carted off to hospital. Nothing could be done about my nose, which remains bent and deformed to this day, but I have never forgotten the lesson I learned. Hit first, hit hard and keep at it until the other bloke goes down and stays down.

I said goodbye to Portland early in 1955, when I was called up for compulsory military service. I couldn't figure out why the British Army needed ex-Borstal boys, but I suppose cannon-fodder (no joke intended) is always welcome. Or perhaps they were running out of Generals, Whatever the reason, I found myself in Catterick Camp in Yorkshire, Signal man No. 23104525 Cannon J.D., 7th Training Regiment, Royal Corps of Signals.

I had already spent nearly a couple of years in a semimilitary environment, so I should have slotted into the Army without too much trouble. Unfortunately I fell foul of the second lowest form of animal life in HM Forces, namely the Lance Corporal in charge of my section. He had obviously seen my records and knew that I came from Borstal, also my broken nose and general air of tough cockiness weren't to his liking, as he never tired of telling me. He was forever making snide remarks about 'decent lads being forced to associate with criminals'. I swallowed all this for some time but it couldn't go on indefinitely.

Matters came to a head one day on the rifle range. We

were doing target practice, and I was laying on my stomach facing the targets when he started rucking me. He was standing behind me and to my left. I rolled over and brought the rifle round until it was pointing directly at him.

'Shut your fucking mouth,' I said. 'Stop digging me out or I'll let you have it in the guts.'

He went white and started to twitch. I almost laughed at the spectacle, although inside I was seething. My finger trembled on the trigger. At that moment I was capable of murder. Then, because I had either to carry out my threat or put the gun down, I lowered the rifle. The second I did so, the scream went up and NCOs ran in from all directions. I was dragged to the guardhouse and, in the ensuing punch-up a lot of military furniture was wrecked. In the end I was overwhelmed by sheer weight of numbers.

That episode marked the end of my military career, which had lasted precisely six weeks. I had, according to my discharge papers, 'failed to fulfil Army requirements', which I reckon a polite way of describing my behaviour. Luckily I wasn't charged with attempted murder. On the 1st March 1955 I was back in Civvy Street among my old mates in the Dale, where I was welcomed with open arms.

I decided to look around and take my time in deciding what sort of villainy I would get up to. The tempting window displays of jewellers and furriers provided the answer. I teamed up with a couple of characters who were supposed to be experts at the smash and grab.

Our first job was a fiasco. We had marked down an ideal target, a jeweller's shop with a valuable collection of tom all on trays behind the glass. It was a simple matter of smashing the window, grabbing the trays and having it away. Or at least that's what we thought. In a stolen van, from which we had removed the rear doors, we descended on the scene in the middle of the afternoon. One of my mates was at the wheel, the other in the back with me, We were gloved up and wearing stocking masks.

A smash and grab operation has to be carried out at speed, and every second counts. The driver swings the van across the front of the shop and then reverses so that the open back is right against the window. Using a pickaxe, I smash in the window but in my enthusiasm I knock the trays back into the shop, where they are beyond my reach. By this time the driver has counted up to five, rams the car into gear and is off down the street, bouncing off other vehicles and scaring the hell out of the pedestrians. The job is a dead loss.

We didn't give up. A few days later we repeated the process, but this time I used a club hammer to break the glass. I came unstuck again. When I cased the shop I hadn't noticed that there was a sort of second window suspended on chains, which was designed to sweep the trays of tom back into the shop in case of a smash and grab. Once more we had to flee empty-handed. We were clearing the windows alright, but in the wrong direction.

After that little lot we decided to give jewellery a miss and concentrate on furs. I sorted out a suitable shop where there was a really smashing mink stuck on a dummy right in the centre of the window. We had nicked a large Humber Snipe saloon for this job. We pulled up outside the furriers' and my mate, swinging a pickaxe, sprinted across the pavement. Within a few seconds the window was a heap of broken glass. As he stood guard to discourage any have-a-go merchants who might be about, I dived into the window to claim the pussy. The bloody thing was fastened to the dummy with what seemed like hundreds of pins. As I tugged at the coat, one of the sleeves came away in my hands.

By this time the furrier had come to the conclusion that there was a maniac in his window tearing his stock to pieces, and was coming forward to do something about it. I wasn't going to lose out on this caper. Grabbing the dummy, coat and all, I jumped out of the window and shot across to the car, followed by my mate swinging the pickaxe. There was a lot of screaming and shouting from the crowd which had gathered. They probably thought it was a kidnapping, seeing what looked like a bird in a fur coat being stuffed into a car by a couple of masked thugs. We made our getaway, but it was a pretty shabby mink which we delivered to the buyer, with whom we had already agreed a price. He knocked a bit off for the damage, but we came out on the right side.

We eventually got it together as a team and earned a nice few quid. Our early experiences taught us to be prepared for the unexpected, and we were lucky on several occasions when a bit of quick thinking got us out of bother. There was one job, however, where luck deserted us altogether.

We had been put on to a warehouse job, a wholesale snouters, which we planned to hit in the early hours of the morning. It was in a deserted area and looked like a doddle. We nicked a large van with a roll-up shutter at the back, copped for a stout plank from a building site and went to work.

The technique of warehouse-breaking is to back the van up against the entrance doors, put one end of the plank against the lock, reverse the van at full throttle and smash the doors in. That's the theory. What happened in this case was that the plank splintered and the bloke who was holding it got the sharp end through the thigh. It was a terrible wound. We didn't dare pull out the massive splinter for fear of doing more damage. With the poor sod lying in the back of the van and yelling his head off, we made for the nearest hospital.

When we got there we carried him inside the casualty entrance, made a commotion and scarpered. It all came out right in the end and the fellow survived, but he will carry a monstrous scar for the rest of his life. Sixty stitches were needed to put his leg together again.

Another caper that didn't produce the expected result was a warehouse job when I made one with Yocker Robinson and Jack McVitie. Jack, who was known as The Hat, was later to be the victim of murder, and Reggie Kray was sentenced to life for the crime. We had reliable information that this warehouse was full of first-class woollen gear, sweaters and suchlike, which would have a ready sale among the market traders who were always happy to pick up a bargain and no questions asked. We decided to have a lorry load of this merchandise and, since we were dead skint, the sooner we claimed it the better.

Yocker was given the job of nicking a covered lorry, and the three of us set out in the early morning. The lorry was parked in a side street near the warehouse and, while Yocker and Jack kept a look-out, I crept round the back to find a way in. I came across a handy window which gave way to some coaxing with a crowbar and quickly nipped inside.

The place was packed from floor to ceiling with large cartons. I put my hand inside one of them and felt soft, woolly material. This was the goods alright. I opened the wide doors of the warehouse, Yocker backed in the lorry and, while Jack kept an eye on the street outside, the two of us crammed the gear in until the vehicle was packed to capacity. We had it away without any trouble, dumped the load in Yocker's garage and got rid of the lorry. We had already made arrangements to shift the loot with a chap called Bobby Parker so, while Yocker went off to fetch him, Jack and I had a wash and brush up and a much-needed cuppa. When Bobby turned up we bowled along to the garage. 'Right. Lets have a look at the gear,' said Bobby.

I opened one of the cartons and Bobby pulled out some of the contents. They were not woollen sweaters but socks, multi-coloured, diamond-patterned socks, thousands of them.

'Christ,' said Bobby, 'what do I do with this lot? There's enough socks here to kit out a bloody army.'

To give him his due, Bobby was a grafter. He knocked out the whole load, but at a fraction of the price we would have got for sweaters. For months afterwards it was easy to recognise Bobby's friends and acquaintances. They all wore multi-coloured, diamond patterned socks.

CHAPTER FOUR

ELLEN:

My real grandfather on my father's side was killed in the first World War, so I never saw him. His widow, my nan, re-married, this time to what we called a foreigner, although he had lived in the Dale for years. He was a Sicilian, one of a colony who had settled in Bangor Street in the early part of the century. I don't rightly know why they came to England or how they chose the Dale as their home. They were ice-cream sellers and organ grinders, and I suppose a Bangor Street slum was heaven to them as compared to their peasant roots in the island of Sicily.

My step-grandfather was a swarthy-skinned man with a large curly moustache who spoke English after his own fashion with a lot of arm-waving. I understood about one word in four when he talked to me. He was always on about the Cosa Nostra, which my nan told me were Sicilian bandits whose principal occupations were robbery and murder. Later on in life I was to come in contact with some of their descendants, sharp-suited men from America who were members of the international conspiracy known as the Mafia. Whether my step-grandfather was with or against this Cosa Nostra was not quite clear to me at the time, but then there were lots of things which I didn't fully understand.

We were going through a bad time at home, what with dad being away and all that. I helped out as much as I could but on my wages of thirty bob a week, one pound fifty pence in today's money, my contribution to the family fortunes couldn't be said to be enormous. What with work and evening classes my days were pretty well filled up, but I missed my Joe. He wasn't a great letter-writer but I did get occasional short notes from him from which I gathered that he was keeping his head above water in Borstal. There were times when I tried to imagine what it was like for him and I asked questions of some of the lads from the Dale who had gone through the Borstal experience. From what they told me I guessed that Joe was tough enough to survive. Anyway he was transferred from one institution to another when he was called up for military service, having reached the age of eighteen. He sent me a letter from Catterick in Yorkshire where he was serving with the Royal Corps of Signals.

While Joe was away I spent quite a bit of time with his family. Dad was a very nice man who worked for the local electricity company. He was as straight as a die and I was very fond of him. Joe's mother, who was also called Ellen, was a second mum to me and gave me a lot of useful advice when I took my troubles to her. I also had the support of Joe's elder brothers, Nobby, Tommy and George, who were always around when needed. All three of them were at it in one way or another. Nobby was a real Dale character, forever wheeling and dealing in the markets and building up a nice little empire. Tommy was a grafter and like Joe had no respect for other people's property. If it wasn't nailed down he'd capture it. Billy was a well-known local boxer who often appeared at Mancini promotions at Lime Grove. He never got to be a top-liner but he could be relied on to put up a good show whenever he stepped into the ring. He had a strong following in the Dale. Joe's Army service didn't last long, six weeks to be exact. The Army was quick to discover that he wasn't soldier material and threw him out before he had time to disaffect his fellow conscripts. Why he wasn't sent back to Borstal was a mystery. Maybe he wasn't the flavour of the month there as well. Anyway, in the spring of 1955 he was back in the Dale ready to take up where he left off two years earlier.

One thing I have discovered about about men like my Joe is that they never confide in their women. They leave them to find things out for themselves. I didn't know what Joe was up to. He would disappear for days at a time then suddenly turn up with plenty of money. We would live the life of Riley for a few days, nothing too good for either of us, then he would be off again with his mates. It wasn't my place to ask questions so I didn't ask them. Just the same, stories came back to me via the local gossips which left me in no doubt that Joe was at it in a fairly big way, warehouse breaking, smash and grab raids and breaking and entering. He seemed to have a charmed life and, though his cards were marked by the local police, they could never pin anything on him.

When we were together Joe and I behaved like a typical married couple which to all intents and purposes we were. It was generally understood that some time or other we would get married. For the time being I was quite happy with the present arrangement. I didn't feel lonely during his absences since my time was occupied with work and evening classes. I also filled in a lot of my spare time in reading. Nothing came amiss, I seized on all kinds of books and was a regular visitor at the public library. From my reading I learned of life outside the Dale which stood me in good stead later on when I began to take a more important part in Joe's social life.

Browsing in the library I came across a number of books which dealt with the history of the Dale and turned up some interesting facts. There had always been a strong street market tradition in the area. Portobello Road, known as The Lane, was a typical example as was the Norland Road market. Every type of merchandise was sold from the stalls, which were set up every morning and taken down at night. The owners of these stalls were a special breed of men and women, all of them self-employed and very independent. They worked from crack of dawn until late at night and some of them made fortunes. They worked on a simple principle, buy cheap and sell cheap, and they never lacked for customers. They were a godsend to the poor of the neighbourhood.

Norland Road market was closed down to make way for the Westway flyover, but The Lane still exists and is now known all over the world. Part of the road has been taken over by antique dealers who do a roaring trade with the tourists who flock there at week-ends, but the northern end hasn't changed in decades. It is crowded with fruit and vegetable stalls and thronged with bargain hunters, the air is full of exotic odours from the West Indian restaurants and cafes which have sprung up like mushrooms and the stallholders still bellow in the time-honoured way. I had been brought up amongst the noise and the bustle but I still was excited by it all.

On my visits to the library I went through the daily papers which were there in plenty from the tabloids to the superior ones like the Times and the Telegraph. I didn't bother much with the political news. So far as I was concerned it was a load of old rubbish. I did spend some time with the crime reports because I wanted to know what was happening in that area. There was no lack of news. The gang wars were at their height in the mid-fifties and the papers were full of the criminal exploits of such as the Messina brothers, Billy Hill,

Jack Spot and their respective gangs. The reports were mostly garbled but I read between the lines, linked it with the gossip in the Dale and so got a pretty clear picture of what was going on.

Later on, when Joe became part of that picture, I was to meet many of these characters, so I was well prepared. Actually I did come into contact with the Messina operation. The four brothers had cornered the trade in vice in the West End and were always on the lookout for fresh talent. One of their scouts had the idea of looking for it in the Dale. I was just the sort of girl they preyed on, eighteen years old, pretty and neat and tidy. Anyway this pratt decided to chat me up as I was leaving work one evening and, instead of telling him to piss off, I played along with him. He told me that I was sitting on a fortune and he could show me the way to make one. He didn't mention the snags like venereal disease and the fact that most of the fortune would disappear into the pockets of his bosses.

I made a date with him for the following night in a pub in Notting Hill Gate and rushed round to the Cannon's to see if Joe was about. He was away on one of his mysterious jobs, but Nobby and Tommy, were at home. I told them the story and they laughed their heads off, but they were obviously put out by the news that the Messina's were trespassing on what they regarded as their territory. To cut a long story short, I didn't keep the appointment, but the Cannon brothers did. They picked a fight with the pratt, Nobby duffed him up, the two of them dragged him outside and Tommy, who carried a knife and knew how to use it, altered his face for him.

After that little incident the Messina touts kept away from the Dale. As Nobby later explained to me, they weren't real villains, just a bunch of dirty ponces who hated the sight of blood, particularly if it happened to be theirs. Anyway, he said, the Messinas were on their way out. The law was on to them and it was only a matter of time before they were busted.

Although I didn't have any real experience of life outside the Dale I knew that it existed. The trouble was that it was hard to find the time to explore other neighbourhoods. Every new day presented its problems and, small though they were, they had to be coped with. I was streetwise by the standards of the Dale but my knowledge of what went on outside was mostly gained from reading. I never thought much about the future. There were times when I indulged in day-dreaming, the little house in the country with a garden and kids to look after and that sort of thing, but the day to day struggle to survive was more important than day-dreams.

In the daily journey to work and during the time I was at my employment I had ample opportunity to see what it was like in that other world outside the Dale, and believe me it really was another world. All my reading only gave me a sketchy idea of what went on. I knew my Joe was deeply involved in it, that he was breaking away from the Dale, dressing in smart clothes and spending much of his time in the West End. I think I must mention at this stage that he was a hard man. Very strong physically and a terror in a fight. Nobody with any sense took a liberty with him. They were on a hiding to nothing.

It was about this time that my social life became more crowded, because for some reason best known to himself, Joe began to invite me out in the evenings. We went to a few clubs in the Paddington area where he appeared to be quite well-known to both the proprietors and the clients. It was a new and strange world to me and for a time I felt uncomfortable amongst these people who obviously had plenty of money and were used to the life. For a time I was like a duck out of water but I watched points, didn't open my mouth too much and soon developed a taste for the high life.

I tumbled to what Joe was up to on a certain evening when we went to the Miramar, a very nice club just off the Edgware Road. It was owned by a married couple called Challoner and Dulcie, the wife, was a very nice woman with whom I became great friends. That particular night there was a very flash type putting himself about and making a real nuisance of himself. George Challoner tried to have a quiet word with this character but it didn't seem to do any good. He still kept shouting the odds and using bad language. I saw George look over at my Joe and nod his head. Joe was up on his feet in an instant. He walked quickly over to the scene of the trouble and said a few quiet words to Jack the Lad. I couldn't hear what was said, but it obviously upset the flash fellow who took a swing at Joe.

It was all over in a matter of seconds. Joe easily avoided the punch aimed at him and replied with a short jab to the fellow's chin and, without pausing, literally carried him to the door of the club and took him outside. George came over to me and told me not to worry, Joe would be back in a couple of minutes. Sure enough, hardly had he finished speaking when Joe came back to the table.

'Alright?' said George.

'No trouble,' replied Joe.

George patted Joe on the shoulder and left us.

'What was all that about?' I asked.

Joe laughed. 'Just doing my job,' he said.

I must have looked puzzled, because he went on to explain what 'doing his job' meant. Club owners, he

said, sometimes ran into a spot of bother. For a variety
of reasons they weren't anxious to call in the police and
relied on strong-arm men to deal with trouble. They
were known as minders. Joe had joined their ranks. It
was the first time ever that Joe had taken me into his
confidence about the way he earned his living.

CHAPTER FIVE

JOE:

In the mid-fifties London was the scene of terrible outbreaks of violence, with rival gangs of Greeks, Maltese and local villains fighting for control of gambling and prostitution. Everybody carried a knife or a gun. Some carried both, and shootings and stabbings were regular events in the clubs and spielers which had sprung up in Soho and the East End. Even in the plush nightspots of Mayfair the rival mobs fought out their bloody battles.

Among the notorious faces was Billy Hill, the governor of the West End, and Jack 'Spot' Comer, another contender for the top jolly's position. George Caruana was top man among the Maltese. He was laying the ground for a take-over from the Messina brothers, whose careers as ponces were drawing to a close under the threats of repeated nickings by the Old Bill. Thay had had a good run for their money and made themselves vast fortunes in the vice rackets.

There were many other assorted villains about, but there was no doubt who was the boss. Billy Hill, who had like myself done a stint in Portland (class of '27 as the Yanks would say), was at the top of the heap. He had come up the hard way but, although he had served several sentences, including a stretch in Dartmoor, he had really made crime pay. Among the jobs that were down to him were a bullion robbery at London Airport in 1947, the Eastcastle Street Post Office in 1952 and the KLM gold robbery in 1954. The rewards from these three jobs alone must have run into six figures. He wasn't nicked for any of them.

A favourite meeting-place for villains at this time was Lyons' Corner House in the Strand, not far from Charing Cross station. It was open day and night, but the mobs gathered in the early morning hours. I was there once with a couple of mates when a mob from South London began to take liberties. It looked as though we were on a hiding to nothing, but three fellows at a nearby table came to the rescue. They were the Kray twins, Ronnie and Reggie, and a hard case by the name of Tommy Smithson.

I had known Ronnie and Reggie for some time, but I had never met Tommy, though we later became good friends. He had a good-looking blonde girl-friend called Fay Richardson and owned a spieler in Berwick Street in the heart of Soho. He was a great favourite with the local brasses, who used to take their troubles to him. He was always ready with a shoulder to cry on or a handy tool to give them another sort of consolation. It was his habit of holding out the helping hand that led to his death.

What happened was that his girl-friend Fay, later to become notorious as Fay 'Kiss of Death' Sadler in the Pen Club murder in 1960, was banged up in Holloway on a charge of 'kiting' or passing dud cheques. Tommy put the bite on George Caruana for funds for her defence, but the wily George wasn't having any. On a fine afternoon in June 1956, Tommy called at Caruana's house in Carlton Vale with the intention of collecting.

Caruana was not at home, but Tommy came face-to-face with a pair of Maltese ponces, Philip Ellul and Victor Spampinato, both associates of Caruana. Ellul was carrying, and two shots put an end to the career of Tommy Smithson. One hit him in the shoulder. The other struck him in the neck, severing the carotid Artery. Tommy died in the gutter. His funeral was a splendid affair attended by a host of villains and about three-quarters of the prostitute population of Soho. 'Kiss of Death' Fay, the cause of all the trouble, was among those not present.

My career a minder was doing quite nicely. I flitted from one club to another in the Lancaster Gate and Queensway areas. The money was good and I didn't have much aggravation. All the villains knew me and my connections, so they took care not to step out of line. The ordinary punters were no trouble. If they misbehaved, a couple of sharp slaps would put them right.

I soon earned a reputation as a reliable man, and my services were in demand. I settled on two clubs in the Paddington district as the best paying propositions. One of them was the Conduit owned by Ronnie Costello, a run-of-the-mill drinker open from 3 pm to 11 pm. The other was the Miramar, owned by George and Dulcie Challoner. This was a late night supper club, well furnished with cabaret and a good class of member.

A good minder is essential to the proper running of a club or nightspot. He is not just a heavy, though he must be handy with his fists in case of serious trouble. His real function is to smell out aggravation and put a stop to it before it develops into a battle. The owner of the club should not be involved in this. For instance one fellow I knew would wade in with flying fists at the first hint of bother which was definitely the wrong way to go about things. Since he was about six feet four and built like a brick shithouse, his appearance alone was enough to frighten most people.

His name was Tiny Evans, and he visited the Miramar quite regularly. I dropped into his club one evening for a quiet drink and noticed that one of the clients had trouble written all over him. When the balloon went up Tiny performed as usual, but the bloke was a rough handful and Tiny had quite a job chucking him out. Coming back into the club looking the worse for wear, Tiny sorted me out and gave me a rucking in front of all the customers.

'Why didn't you give me a hand?' he said. 'You could see I was in bother.'

'Leave it out, Tiny,' I replied. 'I don't work here. You should get yourself a good minder.'

This remark seemed to get up his nose. He went on a bit, poking me in the chest with his finger. Such liberties I don't allow. I gave him a couple of right-handers, he went down and I left the premises. The following day he had me nicked for assault, which cost me fifteen quid in fines and compensation at Marylebone Magistrates' Court.

The point of this story is to show that there are certain people who should never be in the club business. They are fond putting themselves about, but when the crunch comes they run screaming to the law. This maybe does something to restore a bruised ego, but it does nothing at all for a man's reputation.

Jack Spot was one of the clients at the Miramar. He lived nearby in Hyde Park Mansions at the corner of Edgeware Road and Sussex Gardens. His wife Margaret, known as Rita, was often with him. She was a strikingly good-looking woman and she thought the world of Jack. He was having some aggravation at the time, in fact he had just come through a trial at the Old Bailey which had attracted a great deal of press publicity. As a result he was keeping a low profile.

The story behind the trial was common knowledge in the underworld. Billy Hill had returned from one of his foreign trips to find that Jack had been putting himself about and claiming that he was the governor of the West

End. This didn't please Billy at all. On August 11th 1955, in Soho's frith Street, Jack earned himself a vicious striping at the hands of Albert Dimes (real name Alberto Dimeo one of Billy's trusted lieutenants. Dimes himself didn't escape injury. Jack had plenty of bottle and could be relied upon to give as good as he got. The two of them appeared at Marlborough Street and were committed for trial at the old Bailey.

There were two trials, both of them farces, which ended in Spotty and Dimes being chucked and leaving the court with no (further) stains on their characters. There had been a touch of the Damon Runyon's about the second trial, with mentions of Sonny the Yank, Moisha Blue Boy and a reverend gentleman by the name of Basil Claude Hudson Andrews who, as well as being a retired clergyman, was a very accomplished liar.

Jack Spot approached me just after Christmas with an offer to become his minder. While I was very happy at the Miramar, fifty quid a week in the hand was not to be sneezed at. I had a feeling that I might be letting myself in for a load of grief but it was a step up the ladder and into the big league, so I took the job.

Actually it wasn't too bad, in the beginning at least. Only the best was good enough for Jack, and it rubbed off on me. He was always well-tailored, went to the best places, and I began to see at first hand how the other half lived. When he went on a meet I would be at his elbow, keeping a sharp eye open for signs of trouble. There was only one fly in the ointment. Jack was the most tight-fisted geezer I had ever come across. He would be sitting in a pub, with everybody buying rounds, but he never put his hand in his pocket. At times the situation became so embarrassing that I would go to the bar and get them in. When we got back to the flat he made no effort to pay me what I laid out, but would say 'here's a present for you, Joe' and bung me a silk tie. I collected scores of these momentoes, but the only time I saw readies was at the end of the week when I got my wages. I reckoned that Jack had bought up a job lot of these ties to give away as tips.

Through Jack I made several useful contacts and did a bit of minding for some of them, which is how I came to be sitting in a Knightsbridge drinker one day with a couple of his friends, straight businessmen called Terry Jennings and Patrick Ryan. I believe they were carrying a large amount of cash, which was why my presence was necessary. Anyway, there I am, sipping a light ale and at peace with the world, when I look in the mirror and see the reflection of Paddy Onions, a villain from South London, holding a chopper with which he is about to split my skull open.

I don't waste any time in taking a dive to one side as the chopper comes down and bites into the table top, but I am hampered by the arms of the chair and can't get up. Onions and his mates, three tearaways from the same manor, set about me with knifes and razors as I do my best to protect myself with my arm across my face. There is blood everywhere. Ryan has passed out and Jennings is having it away on his toes. There is a lot of screaming and shouting from the customers and some yelling on the part of the staff of the club, who don't care for the sight of a good punter being chopped up on the Axminster. Finally they scarper and I stagger to my feet, literally soaked in the red stnuff

A couple of the girls did what they could to tidy me up, but I knew I had to get to a hospital pretty quickly as I was losing a lot of blood. There was no question of waiting for an ambulance and interrogation by the Old Bill. I reel out into Knightsbridge and I was lucky to get a taxi to take me to St. Mary's hospital in Paddington.

I bunged the driver a good few quid to make up for the bloodstains on the seat and dived into the casualty, where they did a rapid job of hemstitching. I made up a fanny about being attacked and robbed, gave them a phoney name and address and got the hell out of it.

The best thing for me to do now was to go home, where I could rest up and keep out of the way for a while. When I walked in the door looking like something out of a horror film, poor old Mum nearly passed out and my girl Ellen, who happened to be there, gave me a mouthful, most of which I didn't listen to. After all, I wasn't complaining. I didn't see why anyone else should.

The news that I had been done went round the manor like wildfire. Some of my mates suggested a revenge raid over the water, but I had my own ideas about that, so I told them to leave it out. The wounds healed up fairly quickly, I took the stitches out myself and I was as good as new apart from a few scars. Since most of the cutting was done with razors, these scars were hardly noticeable.

I did a few more jobs through Spotty's introductions, but they were dead easy. One of them was to look after a woman club owner who was having aggravation from a couple of so-called villains. Her name was Barbara Knox-Marsh and she was partners in an exclusive Mayfair nightclub called the Blue Angel. I put in an appearance there for a few nights, which was enough to put the wind up this pair of toe-rags. As soon as they set eyes on me they knew they were out of their class and they faded out of the picture.

Some time later Barbara Knox-Marsh was found dead in her office at the club. She had taken an overdose of sleeping tablets. It was curious that two of her friends involved in the nightclub scene also met tragic ends.

Esmee Noel-Smith, owner of Esmeralda's Barn, died of coal-gas poisoning and her friend Linda Justice committed suicide. Maybe the going was too tough for them. There was one woman whose nerve didn't give under the strain. She was Billy Hill's wife Aggie, who ran a club called the Modernnaires and had more than one finger in other establishments. As I remember she was not living with Billy, although they were on good terms with each other. She must have been worth a few bob when she retired and went to live in the Channel Islands.

One of the more interesting jobs that Spotty put me on to was minding Billy Daniels, the Old Black Magic man himself, when he appeared at the London Palladium. I expected to meet a right big head, but he turned out to be one of the best, a real down-to-earth bloke who treated me more like a friend than a minder. He was on bail facing a murder charge back in the States, but it didn't seem to worry him. I must have made a good impression, for he remembered me twenty years later when he visited the twins in Parkhurst. He sent a signed photograph in to me with the message 'Keep your chin up'.

It was in May 1956 that the shit hit the fan so far as I was concerned. It started off at the Roundhouse pub in Norland Market where I had a meet with Jack. I was with my brother Tommy and a fellow called Johnny Webster. Jack told me he was taking Rita out for a meal that evening to a restaurant in Edgeware Road, and the arrangement was that I should meet them there after dinner and go on to the flat with them.

To fill in the time I took Ellen to the Conduit club, which was a few minutes walk from the restaurant where Jack and Rita , were dining. I hadn't seen much of Ellen for some time what with one thing and another, so it was a bit of an occasion. Ellen was my steady, like myself one of a large family and living on the same manor. Her old man was a local character who had been very tasty in his time.

Ellen and I had a lot to talk about and the time passed quickly. I'd had a good few drinks and, when I looked at my watch, it was one o'clock in the morning, long past the time when I was due to meet Jack and Rita. Still, there was no use crying over spilt milk, so I spent the rest of the night with Ellen.

In a way I was lucky. If I had been with Jack when he made his way home I would have been dead or, at best, seriously injured, for this was the night when Jack Spot was the victim of one of the most savage and brutal attacks in the history of gang , warfare. As Jack and Rita, arm in arm, approached the main entrance to the block of flats where they lived, a crowd of men ran from the shadows and closed in on them. According to Rita, who told me the whole story, there were at least six, and she swore that one of them was Billy Hill. I couldn't believe that. Billy was no coward, but he wouldn't put himself up front if there was any chance of being identified. He had too much at Stake to risk that.

However that may be, the mob certainly made a mess of Jack. They were tooled up with knifes, razors, coshes and iron bars, and in the space of a few minutes they had marked him for life. His face was slashed to ribbons, he was stabbed in the body and beaten about the head and shoulders. Rita, who was as game as they come, tried to defend her husband but was felled by a blow from a club. The attackers fled, leaving Jack stretched out on the pavement in a pool of his own blood.

I went round the hospital first thing the following morning with Rita. Jack was lying there under police guard, his face completely covered with bandages. He was in considerable pain but he knew he had to do some fast thinking because Rita had put up some names to the Old Bill. Out of hearing of the copper I managed to have a few whispered words with Jack. I want you to go and see Hill, Joey,' he said. 'Tell him that Rita wants to nick the mob who did me. Tell him I'll talk her out of it if he agrees to stop the aggravation. Will you do that?'

I had no choice. I was known as Jack's minder and it wouldn't be long before people would come looking for me. I got in touch with Hill and made a meet with him at his office in Warren Street, just off the Tottenham Court Road. I knew I was going into the lion's den, so I took the precaution of tucking a .45 into the waistband of my trousers.

As I picked my way through the crowds of motor dealers packing the pavements of Warren Street I wasn't too happy. I was even less happy when I went into Hill's office. Billy was waiting for me with Dimes standing beside him and about a dozen members of the firm standing around. Nobody searched me, which was a mistake on their part; or perhaps Billy didn't want the shooting to start before he had heard the news from Spot.

I passed on the message that Jack had given me and, to tell the truth, I was surprised at the way Hill took it. He was normally very calm, and kept his temper even under extreme provocation. Now he was shouting and almost foaming at the mouth. 'I dont make deals with grasses,' he yelled. 'Listen son, you're lucky not to be in the next fucking bed to Spot. If it wasn't for Frankie Fraser putting in a good word you fucking would have been. You leave this one out, Spot's a wrong 'un. You side with him and you'll get the same treatment.'

I didn't like the way things were working out. It was all going wrong, and there was too much chat about hospitals for my liking. I unfastened my jacket in case I needed to make a quick grab for the shooter and Dimes noticed the movement. He guessed that I was carrying and knew that if it came on top he and Billy would be the first to cop a bullet. He cut into the conversation .

'Look, Joe,' he said. 'All we're interested in is seeing that nobody gets nicked down to this. Can you get a couple of our boys in to see Spot and fix things up?'

It all sounded very reasonable. Jack would be in no danger with the Old Bill watching over him, so nothing but good could come out of the scheme. Billy had nothing more to say, and Dimes nominated two blokes to go in the hospital with me. One of them was Jimmy Woods who was well-known to me. I had never met the other fellow. We made a meet for the next day at the Fifty One club, which was close to the hospital.

I went to see Jack straight away. I was in a dodgy situation because I had to box clever and pretend that I hadn't seen Billy. Jack agreed to see the two fellows to discuss taking the heat off the mob, but was very worried that Hill didn't seem to want to know. His main concern was Rita's safety. I promised him I would watch out for her.

I turned up at the Fifty One as arranged, and Billy was there with Jimmy Woods and the other fellow. I left for the hospital with the two of them and Billy said he would wait lor us at the club. When we saw Jack the discussion didn't take long. He was pleased to see Jimmy, who had once worked for him, and he listened carefully to what was said. It wasn't easy with the Old Bill earwigging at the end of the bed, but it was agreed that there would be no point in nicking Fraser and the rest of the mob. Jack promised that he would persuade Rita not to go ahead.

I came away from the hospital well satisfied. As we

turned to leave the ward, Jack called Jimmy Woods back.

'Seen anything of Billy Hill lately'?' he enquired.

'No, Jack. Haven't seen him for months,' said Jimmy.

That was what put the cat among the pigeons. As we came out of the hospital gates there was Billy in his car, surrounded by pressmen. The cunning bastard had set the whole thing up. The evening papers were full of it, how Billy had met three men outside the hospital, with full descriptions of me and the others and a lot of speculation as to why Billy was on the scene at that particular moment. When I saw Jack on the morning after the meet, he was livid.

'You've fucking dropped me right in it, Joe,' he said. 'You let that bastard Hill take a right liberty.'

I tried to explain that I was the one in the middle and had only done my best to sort things, but it didn't wash. I realised then that I wasn't in the same division as Spot and Hill when it came to pulling strokes. The result was that Rita went ahead with her plan for revenge and five men copped for large doses of porridge at the Old Bailey. In June, Mad Frankie Fraser and Bobby Warren were weighed off for seven years apiece and in October Billy Boy Blythe got five and two other blokes, Dennis and Rossi, got fours. I wasn't involved in any of this. Rita was being minded by a very efficient mob known as the Metropolitan Police and had no need of my services.

As far as my own position was concerned I had to do some hard thinking. If Billy had the needle to me I could expect some come-back. Although I had a bit of a reputation, I was only a kid of nineteen on his own and stood no chance if I was fronted by the Hill firm. As it happened, there were some interested parties who had it in for Hill, and when they came to me with the offer of two grand if I would have a pop at him, I took it on. In the early hours one morning I waited in a car outside the Modernnaires. I knew that Hill and Dimes were inside. It was just a matter of waiting until they came out.

They eventually appeared at about three o'clock, Hill and Dimes and two of the mob. My driver started up and, as we sped past the group, I loosed off five shots with the .45. I had never fired from a moving car before and that, combined with the recoil of the heavy-calibre pistol, affected my aim. Hill, Dimes and company were lucky. So was I, because if I'd done any of them it's a racing certainty that I would have been up at the Bailey on a murder charge.

I reckon that Hill knew that I was the culprit. So did the Old Bill, but there was no reaction from either. Maybe Billy felt that it was beneath his dignity to declare war on a nineteen-year-old, and the Old Bill couldn't have had the necessary evidence to secure a conviction. It all came right in the end. Dimes contacted me and offered me a good drink if I would have nothing more to do with Spotty. I took it, and there the whole thing finished.

For poor old Jack it was the end of the road. He was involved in a wounding case where it was alleged that he striped Tommy Falco outside the Astor club, but this was such an obvious fit-up that it was chucked at the Old Bailey. He later opened a club in Bayswater, but that went up in flames shortly after the first night.

There were a few sick jokes circulating in the underworld at the time. Two samples. Billy Hill's the governor. Jack Spot was very cut-up about it' and 'Did you know Spotty was born two days before the Titanic went down. Two fucking disasters within forty-eight hours'.

Looking back now at the kid I was in those far-off days, I can't help laughing. History was being made in

1955. Bank rate went up from three-and-a-half to four-and-a-half per cent (no kidding), Winston Churchill resigned as Prime Minister, there was a general election, the independent television service started up and all sorts ot people were getting worried about the atom bomb. In the middle of all this was young Joey Cannon, unmindful of the earth-shaking events going on around him, swaggering about the West End with a .45 stuck down his trousers and not giving a fuck for anybody or anything. I know it was me, but I find it hard to believe.

I suppose that, when middle-age puts a spare tyre round the guts, we all have thoughts about the good old days.

After the Spot episode I was at a loose end. I didn't fancy qoing back to minding which, as I saw it, put me up front for spankings but at the end of the queue when the rewards were being dished out. What I was looking for was a nice tickle, a quick job that would put a lot of cash in my pocket in a short space of time. It came along in the shape of a snatch that was put up to me by a couple of mates, Roy Simmonds and Ray Jackman.

The plan was to lift the payroll of a large dairy outfit in St John's Wood. It wasn't exactly a snatch, which is capturing money in transit nor was it breaking and entering. It fell somewhere in between. The information came from two inside men employees of the company, who would get a share of the loot when the job was done.

On the face of it there seemed nothing to worry about. We cased the premises one Friday morning and saw two clerks who, we had been told, were responsible for paying out the wages. They would be no trouble. Put the two of them together and they wouldn't make a man. We already had a floor plan of the offices and the yard, and the wages procedure had been explained to us. All we now had to do was go in and lift the reward.

We qo out on the job on the Friday morning. Roy has nicked a taxi which he says is not all that quick but will turn on a tanner. I remark that we're supposed to outrun police cars, not qo round in circles hoping they'll get dizzy and go home. We arrive at the depot and leave Roy in the taxi. I walk to the loading bay with Ray, and leave him there on watch. I put on one of those funny masks, a big red nose fastened to dummy specs that hook over my ears and go up the spiral steps to the door that leads to the wages office. The gun is under my jacket.

I take a deep breath and go throuqh the door. The two clerks are there plus a mob at the window waiting to be paid. One of the clerks goes to grab me so I whip the gun out and hit him over the head with it. I claim the two trays of wage packets and back out of the door.

The gun is in my hand under the trays. With both hands full it's impossible for me to open doors. The quickest way out is through the sterilising department. The news had reached there before me, which isn't surprising, there's a lot of hooting and screaming going on. The women workers, seeing me go tearing through with the false nose hanging off and clutching their wages, begin pelting me with empty bottles. I get through without a scratch, which is a miracle, and rush out into the street at full pelt.

Ray, on watch outside, heard the scream go up and thought I was captured. He is in the cab, looking out through the rear window. As I dash out of the yard, Roy reverses, comes to a halt beside me, I jump in and we're away.

It was a doddle, and over so quick that there wasn't even a chase. The loot amounted to a very healthy sum and, after the two blokes at the yard had their whack, we split the rest three ways. We were all well satisfied.

It was a month later that it came on top. One of the fellows who had given us the info on the job had told his bird all about it, and she grassed us to the Old Bill after they had had a row. All five of us were nicked, and duly appeared in the dock at the Bailey, charged with a variety of offences. In my case it was 'robbery while armed with an offensive weapon'. The prosecution continually suggested that I was in possession of a gun, but it couldn't be proved because nobody had seen the weapon for long enough to swear that it was, in fact, a shooter. Although I had used it to hit the wages clerk over the head, it was then hidden from sight under the trays I was carrying. Just the same, the clerk's injuries proved that some sort of weapon had been used.

We were all found guilty. Raymond Jackman was sentenced to five years, Roy Simmonds got three and the two inside men received two years and four years respectively. I copped for seven, even though I was the youngest member of the group. This was because I was the one who had inflicted the injuries.

Because I was under twenty-one, I was officially what was known as a young prisoner, so I ended up in the YP wing at Wormwood Scrubs, of which I had had previous experience. I was there for a fortnight, but the authorities decided that I was a disruptive influence and transferred me to Pentonville. That suited me fine. I didn't care for the company of kids who were, in the main, petty thieves and juvenile delinquents.

What didn't appeal to me was the prospect of doing seven years bird. Soon after my arrival in Pentonville I sorted out people who I knew and could rely on. Billy Ambrose was one of them, an old-time villain who had once been a boxing champion. He agreed to help me to escape.

Billy was one of the inmates 'on association', that is he was allowed to eat in company with other prisoners and stay unlocked of an evening to play darts, billiards or table tennis. Those of us who didn't have this privilege were served the last refreshment of the day around seven o'clock, just before the association men were locked up for the night. The 'refreshment' consisted of a thick brown milkless and sugar-free sludge known as cocoa and the serving of this treat coincided with the last physical head-count of the day.

I had worked out the plan for a break-out and discussed it with a selected bunch of mates who were serving long sentences. Billy Ambrose would unlock me after cocoa-time, using a key which I would provide. I would then sneak up to the top landing and hide in the water storage tank in the recess. Later, when everything was quiet, I would unlock my mates, we would descend mob-handed on the screws on duty, tie them up and then depart.

Came the day when the key was ready. Albert Hobbs, unofficial locksmith to the nick, passed it to me and I handed it to Billy. Immediately after the cocoa performance I set about making a dummy to fit in my bed so that I would not be missed when the landing screw made his rounds, peering through the peep-hole in the door to check that the inmate had dossed down. I hid the dummy under the bed and then waited for Billy to turn up.

It seemed like hours later that I heard a key turn in the lock, although it could not have been more than fifteen minutes. The door opened and there stood Billy, looking for all the world as though it was quite normal for him to have his own twirl. He pressed the key into my hand and with a 'good luck, kid' he hurried away to join his mates on association. I quickly put the dummy to bed, picked up my shoes and left the cell, locking the

65

door behind me. In stockinged feet I crept along the landing, keeping close to the wall, until I got to the stairs. Now I had to reach the top landing without being seen. Moving carefully and silently I made it.

The huge storage tank in the recess was filled almost to the rim with the coldest water in north-west London. As I lowered myself in I let out a gasp. Sitting it out for four hours wasn't going to be a picnic. The first half-hour was bearable and then the cold started eating into me until even my bones were frozen. There was also another matter I hadn't taken into account but a pint of piss in a hundred gallons of water isn't what you might call excessive pollution.

I had no way of telling the time, but it must have been close on midnight when I felt it was safe for me to leave the tank. I squelched on to the landing and, lying on my stomach, slid to the edge and looked down on the main hall of the block. I wanted to know where the night staff was, so that I could plan my route for the unlocking. I saw one of the screws straight away. Indeed I couldn't have missed him, because he was coming up the stairs to do a routine check of the landing on which I was lying. There is no way I can claim him before he spots me, so there is only one thing for it. I wriggled back to the recess and climbed back into the tank.

Risking a quick look over the rim of the tank, I saw the screw standing and staring at the floor. There at his feet was an enormous Cannon shaped patch of water from which led a trail of wet footprints to my hiding-place. He turned and ran for the alarm bell, and the heavy mob arrived so speedily that I barely had time to dump the incriminating key before I was dragged out of the tank and off to the chokey.

As a result of this caper I was brought before the Governor, charged with attempting to escape. I forget how much remission I lost, but the biggest blow was that I was put into patches. This is a way by which escapers can be easily identified. On to the normal prison dress are sewn bright yellow diamond shaped pieces of material, both front and back of jacket and trousers. Also, a red light burns throughout the night in the cell. As a precaution against further attempts, the con on patches must leave his clothes outside the cell when he is locked up for the night. I discovered that sleeping naked under threadbare blankets in a cold peter isn't exactly funny.

Not long after the escape episode I was in trouble again. I was talking about the diabolical wages we received with Joey Cronk, Alfie Fletcher and a few others from Notting Hill, and we were wondering what sort of protest we could make. I think it was Alfie who came up with the idea of doing the canteen and distributing the loot among the cons.

'It would be dead easy for you, Joe,' he told me. 'You're on patches. You line up by the canteen every morning before you go to work, don't you?'

I agreed that we did just that.

'OK then. You're there for about a half-hour, nobody watching you. All you need is a key.'

'That's easy,' I said. 'There's one at the bottom of the water tank on the top landing.'

'Leave it to me,' said Alfie, 'I'll get it.'

He was as qood as his word, and the key which I had dumped was smuggled to me the next morning. When the men on patches assembled as usual I was the first in line. As soon as the coast was clear I unlocked the canteen door and nipped inside. It was like being in Aladdin's cave. I grabbed a large, empty carton and filled it with snout, sweets, biscuits, jam, tins of fruit and anything else which was handy. It was like winning an 'all you can carry away' contest. A quick look round and I was down the landing to Alfie's peter, where I tipped the lot on to his bed.

'Quick, get rid of this,' I said. 'Back with some more in a minute'

Alfie's eyes lit up like Christmas decorations. I shot back to the canteen with the empty box and refilled it, while Alfie spread the word. I repeated the performance five times, and Aladdin's cave began to look like Mother Hubbard's cupboard. On the sixth trip, disaster struck. I came out of the canteen and ran straight into the arms of the Governor. He looked at the bulging box I was carrying, then over my shoulder to the bare shelves of the canteen. I've never in my life, seen a man look so astonished.

The heavy mob marched me straight into the Governor's Office, who informed me that I would get no more wages until the missing stock had been paid for. All they had recovered, in spite of a full-scale search of every peter in the block, was the box they caught me with. I worked out that, at 2/6 (12.p) a week, I would be in debt for the next fourteen years.

A fortnight later I was nicked again, but this time it was more serious. At the end of the work period, talking was strictly prohibited, a rule enforced with a lot of shouting and bawling on the part of the screws. On this occasion I was in the mailbag shop with Alfie Hinds, keymaker Albert Hobbs, Alfie Fraser and a few others.

When the screw bellowed 'stop talking' I was caught with my mouth open, so to speak. My card had been marked over the canteen incident and the screw, one of the so-called 'hard' men, wasn't going to stand for any nonsense. He walked towards me.

'Didn't you hear what I fucking said,' he yelled. 'Shut your fucking trap, or I'll shut it for you.'

'Bollocks,' I replied.

A roar of laughter went up from the assembled cons. The screw's face turned purple, and he took out his notebook.

'Right, you're for it this time,' he said.

I'd had enough of the verbal. I stuck one on his chin, he went down spark out and the alarm bells began to ring. As the heavy mob stormed in, swinging their sticks, a few of the lads had a go. In no time at all a minor riot was on.

We were eventually subdued and dragged off to the chokey block, but not before a lot of damage had been inflicted on both sides. We came off worst. The riot sticks used by the heavy mob are fearsome weapons. When you've been hit with one of them you don't fancy a second dose.

When we appeared before the Governor, it was all down to me as I was the one who had struck the first blow. The others were awarded various minor punishments such as loss of priviliges or remission but sentence on ringleader Cannon would be passed by the visiting magistrates. They awarded me twelve strokes of the birch.

I didn't know a lot about this birch business. It had been described to me once by a bloke who had a taste of it, but I didn't really listen to him. Now I was to discover at first hand what it was all about. For a start, after the punishment had been awarded, it had to be sanctioned by the Home Secretary. While waiting for this, I was kept in solitary and out of contact with other prisoners.

The next stage in the proceedings, after the prisoner has spent three nail-biting weeks in solitary, is the day when the punishment is carried out. This is known by all the inmates, because they are kept locked up until the ceremony is over, as happens in the case of an execution.

When the day came, the prison was in an uproar. Cons were shouting from behind the doors of their peters, the boob percussion section (tin mugs on tin plates) started up and there was a general hullabaloo which reached a crescendo when I was marched down to one of the workshops where the official assault was to take place. I didn't know what to expect, but in the physical sense I was not afraid. I'd taken some stick in my time. A bit more wouldn't make all that difference.

Wearing only a suit of overalls, beneath which I was completely naked, my bare feet in a pair of slippers, I was led into the shop which had been specially cleared for the occasion. The first object I saw was the 'horse', a massive wooden framework about six feet high with stout members at top and bottom equipped with leather straps. Standing around this contraption, their expressions resembling those of the dirty mac brigade at a strip show, were the Governor, a couple of geezers in white coats who turned out to be doctors, the Principal Officer, a few screws and a small collection of civilians.

The performance started. The escorting screws stripped off my overall's, leaving me stark naked, and shackled me to the horse by the straps. I have never been ashamed of my body but now, surrounded by this crowd of drooling degenerates, I felt degraded and dirty. The screws' hands were everywhere. A broad and heavy leather 'belt was clamped round my waist and a hood placed over my head so that I couldn't see behind me and identify the screw who did the birching, a very wise precaution this, for I would have claimed the fucking whoreson later on.

The principals in this barbaric ritual now took their

places. The Governor stood in front of me with one of the doctors at his side. I couldn't see the other medico. He was probably taking care of the arsehole end.

The Governor spoke. 'Joseph David Cannon, you have been sentenced to twelve strokes of the birch. This is the first.'

SWISH.

Jesus fucking Christ. I felt my body arch in agony. The pain defied description.

'Joseph David Cannon, you have been sentenced to twelve strokes of the birch. This is the second.'

SWISH.

I heard myself yell, get on with it you fucking bastards, the sweat ran down my face, the doctor moved forward.

'Joseph David Cannon, you have been sentenced to twelve strikes of the birch. This is the third.

' SWISH.

Bloody fucking Nora, O my lacerated arse, fuck you all, fuck you, fuck you.....

'Joseph David Cannon,...'

SWISH

'Whoresons, bastards, scumbags, cunts.....'

' Joseph David Cannon. .'

SWISH

Twelve strokes, twelve bloody, fucking awful strokes, my arse and legs were on fire, the contortions of my body had shifted the horse six feet from its original position. They set me free and put lint and plaster over my arse and legs. The Governor faced me. 'The punishment's over now, Cannon. You took it like a man.' He put out his hand. My mouth was full of bile and spittle. I let him have the lot, right in the middle of his boat race.

None too gently the screws put me back into my overalls and slippers and hustled me out of the shop. Some of the spectators were grinning. I learned later that they were observers from the Home Office, present to see that Justice was seen to be done.

Looking back now, with the benefit of hindsight, I am still filled with disgust. I've survived worse beatings at the hands of professionals who know how to hurt. I carry scars all over my body as a result of brushes with underworld enemies. These I can forget; but I will never erase from my mind the organised brutality which, Under the cloak of legality, is perpetrated by a bunch of upper class thugs on the body of a manacled and helpless twenty year old who has committed the heinous crime of punching a pig of a prison officer on the chin. Pain one can forget, but memories last forover.

Having been party to inflicting the injuries, the doctor and his orderlies now seemed extremely concerned to heal them, almost as though they had nothing to do with the original cause. The wounds, a multitude of red and purple weals from waist to thighs, continued to weep blood and fluid for two months. I had to sleep face down, and any incautious movement caused the partly healed scars to open again. I was allowed to bathe frequently. The pink tinge in the water didn't come from the use of bath salts.

Is the birch a deterrent? Does it make a bad boy into a good one? On the evening of the day on which I got the treatment there was a concert in the chapel. It was usual for the blokes in patches to sit on the front row, but for some reason it was decided that we should sit at the back. Johnny Nash, one of the notorious brothers, had provided me with a pillow for my sore arse.

Men on special watch have few privileges, and we tended to hang on to the few that we had. We'll sit in the front, we said. Oh no you won't, said the screws.

We got up and walked out, the rest of the nick followed suit, and the concert was cancelled. So much for the birch as a frightener. It didn't deter me from taking part in a walk-out within eight hours of a birching.

There was one by-product of this filthy business which deserves a mention. My mother came to hear that I had been birched, and immediately came on a visit. Before I was allowed to see her, I was told that I mustn't give any details of my punishment or the visit would be terminated on the spot. To make sure that I didn't say a word out of place a screw stood at my elbow. My mother, who was already distressed, was even more upset when I told her that I couldn't talk about what had happened to me, and she left the nick in tears. When I say that this affected me more than a dozen birchings, I am telling no more than the truth.

There came a time, not long after my wounds had healed, that the Governor of Pentonville made up his mind that he wanted no more of the troublesome Cannon. One afternoon I was collected from the mailbag shop, taken back to my peter and told to get my gear together. The following morning I left for Dartmoor,

I did get a bit of satisfaction during my stay at the Ville. Paddy Onions, who had tried to chop me up in a Knightsbridge club a year previous, was doing a stretch at the time. One morning I claimed him right outside the Governor's office. I was armed with a heavy salt-shaker in a sock, and Onions went down with the first blow, which was hard enough to shatter the solid earthenware of the shaker. I then jumped on him and completed the job by ripping his face to ribbons with the pointed shards that stuck out from the sock. I had waited a long time for my revenge, but it was worth it.

There were fifteen of us on the Dartmoor party, and a shabbier looking lot of miscreants it would be hard to imagine. We wore our own clothes which had been lying screwed up for months - in many cases years - in some forgotten corner of Pentonville. We lined up to be handcuffed. As an added precaution a chain was passed through the fifteen sets of Home Office jewellery, with a screw at each end.

We were loaded into the coach en route for Paddington station, where we would entrain in a reserved carriage for Princetown, As we were shepherded to the platform across the busy concourse we ran the gauntlet of hundreds of curious eyes. I couldn't resist the temptation. A well-dressed City gent stood in the forefront of the onlookers.

'Wotcher, Tom,' I bellowed at the top of my voice. 'When did you get out?'

The rest of the cons joined in, and there were shouts of 'be lucky, Tommy' and 'keep your nose clean'. The City gent, his face puce, made himself scarce and disappeared in the general direction of Mansion House.

'Shut up there and keep moving,' yelled the screw at the rear of the column.

We fell about laughing, and were still giggling as we boarded the train. It's strange, but there was a kind of holiday atmosphere about the proceedings, a relaxation of the tensions of prison life. Even the screws exchanged the odd joke with their charges. In a way it was a break for them too.

The journey to Princetown took something like four hours, and for me at least it was a troublesome one. Ever since I had undergone the flogging had been having trouble with passing water, and needed to visit the lavatory frequently. As we were still chained together, whenever I had to go for a piss there was a right old palaver. First I had to be released from the main chain, then a shorter chain was attached to the cuffs, one end of which was held by the screw. He stood outside the part-closed door while I performed in what might be called a single-handed fashion.

At Princetown we were loaded into the coach that would take us to the prison. The laughing and joking now came to a stop as the chilly mists of the Moor closed in around us. The jail, when we came to it, was grey and forbidding, a huddle of granite buildings stuck out in the middle of nowhere like a scab on the face of Nature. Over the massive entrance doors deep engraved in the stone was the legend 'Abandon Hope all ye who enter here'.

I shall never forget my introduction to the grim pile in which I was to spend several years of my young life. We filed into the Reception, where we shed our clothes, the last link with the outside world, and were issued with the ill-fitting garments that comprised the prison uniform. As I put on these damp, smelly articles I lost my last contact with reality and became part of the nightmare which was Dartmoor.

Let me now describe this hell-hole as I recollect it. The prison building itself was shaped like a horseshoe with the open end facing the main gate. From the round part of the horseshoe branched the wings, four of them, A, B, C and D, but only three wings were in use. C wing had been reduced to rubble by rioting prisoners in 1930. The punishment block and the church also formed part of the main building. The hospital and the workshops were separate. There was a football pitch, a straggle of outbuildings and a gatehouse. A fifteen-foot-high wall enclosed the whole area. It was surprisingly low for a prison wall, but where did the escaper run to when he had gone over it? Miles of treacherous moorland lay between him and freedom.

I spent the first three days in the chokey (punishment) block while somebody somewhere decided where I would go and what sort of work I would do. It shouldn't have been a difficult decision to make, because D wing was reserved for cons who had served four years of their sentences and the choice of work was limited. There was the mailbag shop, where rows of men sat day after day thrusting a large needle through heavy canvas. eight stitches to the inch and a punctured thumb several times a day. Then there was the smithy, a noisy and badly ventilated inferno from which the worker emerged stone deaf at the end of each shift.

Nobody wanted the quarry party. Here gangs of men broke up rocks with sledgehammers, hard manual graft which produced in a week what a mechanical crusher would have turned out in half-an-hour. The works party was a fairly cushy number, their efforts being devoted towards keeping the prison in an upright position. but the cream of jobs was the farm party, where the enterprising bloke could swipe the odd egg or a few spuds or carrots or anything else that was not nailed down.

While waiting allocation the new entrants were seen by the various prison officials. The Governor was the first on the list. His name was Coombes, and he had been nicknamed 'Iron Man' shortly after his appointment to Dartmoor. According to newspaper reports, a hundred discontented cons in the mailbag shop were preparing to riot when the bold Coombes marched in among them and told them to sit down. They did. What the papers didn't say was that Coombes was backed up by fifty screws carrying riot sticks. If the gallant Governor had been on his tod he would have been torn to pieces.

He didn't seem to be all that courageous when I first clapped eyes on him. The room was large - it was actually three cells knocked into one - and the Iron Man sat at a table behind an iron grill, with the Principal Officer by his side and another three or four screws in the background. No way could an aggrieved felon have got at him. He barked a few questions over the distance of eighteen feet which separated us, didn't seem to worry whether I replied or not and I was marched out.

Next on the list was the doctor, and this was a real farce. Drop your trousers. Cough. Right. Next. That was the medical examination. The story goes that one of the cons went sick and was marched in to see him.

'Yes?' barked the medico.

'I'm very worried, doctor. I think I'm masturbating too much.'

'Is anything coming out?'

'Yes, doctor.'

'Right. Carry on.'

When nothing comes out, report sick. Next.'

That was one of the funny stories. There were others, more tragic, of men being left to die in freezing cells. There were no post mortems on the Moor, and only the hardiest survived.

I was fortunate in having several friends already on the Moor who were able to pull a few strings. Billy Ambrose who had played a part in my unsuccessful attempt to escape from Pentonville I was working in the black-smiths shop along with another old mate, Yocker Robinson. The working conditions weren't ideal, but at least it was warm and the screw in charge was an easy - going bloke. Billy put my name up and I was allocated.

I was lucky in avoiding the alternatives, which were the mail-bag shop or the quarry party. The 'no talking' rule on mail-bags had recently been dropped, but was substituted by another which permitted a man to talk to his right-hand neighbour. The stupidity of this was self-evident except to the official mind. What the hell was the use of talking to a bloke who wasn't allowed to reply? The dimwits in charge sorted it out, and came up with the brilliant solution. You could talk to the men on either side, but not those in front or behind! Bloody marvellous!

The quarry party was to be avoided at all costs. Out there, in the depths of winter and with temperatures below freezing, human beings were subjected to the most appalling conditions as they swung sledgehammers on the huge rock-piles which had been blasted from the moorland granite. Occasionally some frenzied con would swing his hammer against the nut of one of the warmly-dressed screws who had unwisely moved too close to him. But why didn't the prison authorities use mechanical crushers? The answer is simple. Slave labour at half-a-crown (12.5p) a week is cheaper.

I was still on the escapers list, and so was put into a peter on the ground floor of A wing. The stone walls dripped water even in the summer, and no amount of mopping-up could clear the constant puddles on the floor. Settling down for the night was an elaborate business. First I would put my clothes outside the door, Then, balancing the bed-board between chair and table, I would put the coir-filled palliasse and pillow on the board. Finally, wrapped in three blankets, I would dry my wet feet, curl up and try to sleep.

My bladder was still playing me up and, though I tried to resist it, the urge to relieve myself several times during the night added to my troubles. The simple business of having a piss was a major operation. The metal pisspot with its ill-fitting lid was within arm's reach and, still swathed in my blankets, I would swing my legs over the side of the bedboard, hold the pot in a convenient position and let go. Considering that all this was done in pitch darkness, it's a miracle I didn't piss all over myself. As it was, there were times when my aim was bad or the pisspot overflowed. The resulting discomfort can be imagined.

The screw who unlocked me in the morning did nothing to make the situation any better. He would wrinkle up his nose and put a disgusted expression on his boat-race,

'Wet the bed again, Cannon,' he would say sneeringly.

Any reply would mean being put on Governor's report, so I kept my mouth shut. The fucking pillock who'd made the remark had come from a warm and comfortable bed after an early rumpo with his old woman. He could well afford to chuckle. It was part of his sensitive and considerate nature.

One of the minor pleasures in a con's miserable life was having a read between locking up and lights out. To enjoy this relaxation it was necessary not only to have a book but also some light to read it by. Books were a problem. They were dished out once a week, three to a cell, irrespective of author or content. Hence a semi-literate bruiser would find himself wading through Tolstoy's 'War and Peace', while in a neighbouring cell an educated con-man would be provided with something like 'Gunfight at Broken Lance Creek'.

As to the lighting, Dartmoor was sweeping into the twentieth century with some startling innovations. When the Prison Commissioners realised that electricity had come to stay the works party was instructed to knock holes in the walls separating adjoining cells. A low-wattage bulb was inserted into the aperture, the two sides were closed up with opaque glass and hey presto!, two peters were lighted at the price of one. Then space-age technology struck a blow for the benefit of the benighted convict. Each peter was equipped with its own light bulb bang in the middle of the ceiling, to be cherished and cared for, polished and talked to, by the occupant.

There was only one snag. Your Dartmoor con, by definition a brute beast with no social conscience, would find himself with a roll-up and no means of lighting it, having run out of matches. Necessity being the mother of invention, the con would twist a piece of toilet paper round a short length of silver foil, jam the foil against the contacts in the bulb holder and create a flame at the same time as he blew the fuses. Half a dozen cells would be plunged into darkness for the rest of the night, but the con would enjoy his smoke.

The day's routine would start when we were unlocked at 7 am. After the 'slopping out', a sick-making performance which I have described elsewhere in this book, we did our best to shave and wash in cold water. The razor-blades issued for shaving were collected in double - quick time in case a suicidal con tried to cut his throat.

We were all perpetually hungry, but the first meal of the day would take the edge off anybody's appetite. There was always porridge, a lumpy mess made from Canadian Pig Meal which tasted of nothing and stuck like glue to the back of the teeth. With this was a cob of bread, a minute pat of margarine and a teaspoonful of jam. This jam, according to reports, was manufactured in the women's prison at Holloway in the same container used to wash the sanitary towels of the inmates.

As an occasional treat we had bacon or goulash. The bacon was carved in incredibly thin slices and cooked in watered fat, and it was little more than a mouthful. The ration for the whole of the nick could have been carved from a live pig and he wouldn't have felt the loss. As for the Goulash, any resemblance to the Hungarian dish of that name was purely coincidental. Made from left-over potatoes, scraps of meat and stale bread, it was formed into a slab, baked and then divided into portions. It looked and smelled like dessicated cowshit.

To wash down the meal there was a pint of coloured water masquerading under the name of tea. It was completely tasteless with a grey scum floating on the surface, but it was wet, warm and welcome.

Work began at eight. Although I was in the warm smithy, I put on all the clothing available to me. A con could be moved from one location to another at a moment's notice, so it was as well to be prepared. I wore a pair of long johns, a vest, two shirts, polo-necked jumper, trousers, overalls, two pairs of woollen socks, a large pair of boots, gaiters, jacket, overcoat and a woollen hat pulled down over my ears. All that could be seen of the original Cannon was a red nose like a beacon poking out from a mass of rags

There were a few hard nuts who believed in tempting Providence. One of them was a chap called Pearce, who was about twenty-five and hailed from Bristol. Even on the coldest days he walked about in an unbuttoned shirt with no vest, and continually ribbed the rest of us. 'What's the matter with you,' he would say. 'What are you all wrapped up for. It isn't cold.' One day he was carted off to hospital with some form of chest infection and died shortly afterward. He found out too late that Moor weather is not to be trifled with.

My work in the smithy wasn't all that hard. Along with Billy Ambrose, Yocker Robinson and the key-maker from the Ville Albert Hobbs, I hammered lumps of metal into various shapes, tended the furnace and generally made myself useful. Albert was always busy making keys and grapnels for blokes who planned to escape. The instructor screw was an amiable bloke who didn't much care what we did so long as we refrained from bothering him. When he was off duty and we copped for one of the discipline screws, we had our own way of dealing with this. A wet sack stuffed up the furnace flue, half a dozen quick pumps on the bellows and the smithy would be filled with dense smoke. The screw then became the target of lumps of iron sailing through the air towards him. He would normally get tired of this performance before we did.

This escape business was almost a way of life for some of the cons. We were kept busy turning out escape tackle, but most of the plans never bore fruit. I reckon that the escapers spent so much time discussing the ways and means that their plot was discovered by the screws before they could put it into action. However, the business of smuggling gear through frequent searches kept the blokes on their toes and provided some excitement in their drab lives.

Of course there were some escape attempts which got beyond the talking stage. Going over the wall presented no real difficulty. It was what waited for you on the other side that made for problems. Guards mounted on ponies patrolled the moors in the vicinity of the prison, and the area was full of natural traps. There were deep holes filled with stinkmud into which a man could fall and disappear in a few minutes without trace, and the constant mist destroyed one's sense of direction.

Two fellows who almost made it were Dennis Stafford and a chap called Day. Staff had had it away before, and got as far as Port of Spain, Trinidad, before being picked up. They went over the wall one misty morning, gambling on the mist clearing later on. It didn't, and they were hopelessly lost. Day was leading the way well ahead of Staff when he suddenly disappeared over the edge of a reservoir, which was his lot.

His body was recovered where it had been trapped by a submerged pipe, which explains why Staff couldn't find him.

I had a word with Staff after he had been nicked in London and sent back to the Moor. He told me that he had searched around for some time trying to find Day. It was of course sheer bad luck that Day had been trapped under the pipe, for otherwise he would have got away with nothing more than a ducking.

Another pair who made a getaway in 1957 were Norman 'Babyface' Ellis, serving 12 years for armed robbery, and Harper Woodward, doing 14 for armed assault. They got well away from the prison, but they were outmatched by fifteen hundred prison officers and coppers, who went over the moors with a fine-toothed comb. A man whose name always came up when escape was under discussion was Ray 'Rubberbones' Webb, who could crawl through the smallest of holes, with the exception of keyholes, and boasted that there was not a nick in the country that could hold him for long. He also made an escape from the Moor but was duly recaptured after a short spell of freedom.

There was one unplanned escape that almost came off. A bloke called Jennings was near the boiler house with one of his mates when an oil tanker was making a delivery. A quick shufti inside the cab and Jennings realised that the driver had left the keys in the ignition. The two men jumped in and roared away, smashing through the rear gates and out on to the road. Pursued by the police, they treated the huge tanker like a cross between a Formula One racer and a Sherman tank, writing off a couple of police vehicles in their juggernaut progress. The tanker finally committed suicide on a treacherous bend and the desperados were captured.

In the smithy we carried on churning out escape

gear, more from habit then anything else. Where they went to I don't know, but there must have been hundreds of items such as keys, grappling ;irons, jemmies and suchlike circulating in the prison, enough for dozens of escape parties. Some of them were discovered by the screws and impounded. They never came back to us.

One of the jobs taken on by the blacksmith was the shoeing of the farm horses, which always provided some amusement. He would be bending over the animal's hoof scraping away with a file when one of us would fire a piece of metal from a catapult at the horse's arse. The huge beast would react to this treatment by having a go at the nearest human object, which was the blacksmith, and proceed to do its best to stomp him into the ground. He developed a remarkable agility for a man of his age.

Work in the shops stopped at eleven thirty when we went in for lunch. This was an unpalatable mess served up in two-tier billy cans, the bottom half holding the main dish while the top half was supposed to contain the sweet. What usually happened was that we ended up with a mixture of stew, potatoes and custard, but since it was all equally foul it wasn't all that important.

There were numerous complaints about the food, but they came to nothing. The Governor had himself tasted the food, found it fit for human consumption and initialled the menu book, and that was that. In order to test the Governor's palate, one of the cons by the name of John Cohen pissed in a cup, tipped it into a container of soup, then called the Iron Man.

'There's something wrong with this soup, sir,' said Cohen.

'It tastes something terrible.'

Coombes dipped a ladle into the soup and took a mouthful.

'Nothing wrong with that,' he declared.

'It tastes like piss to me,' replied Cohen.

The Iron Man poured the rest of the contents of the ladle down his gullet.

'It certainly doesn't taste like piss to me, Cohen.'

'Well it should,because I've just pissed in it,' said Cohen.

The Governor rushed from the wing and Cohen was put on report. He was, by the way, only slightly older than me and was serving twenty years for armed robbery. He had made up his mind to do his bird the hard way, and was constantly up in arms against authority. I came across him twenty years later in Wandsworth. He was still serving the same sentence, which had been added to on account of several misdemeanours, including cutting a screw.

As I have mentioned, I was the youngest prisoner on the Moor, and this had its drawbacks. Today, what with 'gay lib' and 'consenting adults', most youngsters know all about poofs and can spot one a mile off. When the odd lot began to home in on the rosy-cheeked Cannon, silly fucker that I was I thought they were being nice and helpful, but I tumbled what the game was when one of them made a determined attempt to bugger me. These men were anything but limp-wristed sylphs. They were hard men who had been deprived of sex for a long time and, though they had their 'girl' friends among the fairies, they weren't averse to a bit of fresh.

I put a stop to that in double-quick time. I made myself a chiv and stuck it into one of my more passionate admirers. He got the message, and so did the rest of the bum-fuckers. I had no further trouble. in that direction,

Prison Rules lay down that prisoners must be exercised every day just like dogs , so for one hour after the lunch break, winter and summer alike, we trudged round and round the yard between A wing and the hospital. When the rain pissed down, the screws sheltered in convenient doorways. When the snow lay on the ground deep and crisp and even, we sloshed our way through it.

Work ended for the day at four thirty. when a strident hooter sounded. This hooter played an important part in the lives of the prison staff, since it also went off half an hour before the end of the shifts which they worked. It was a well-known fact that the screws had it off with each others' wives, as a certain Sunday newspaper made plain in an article referring to Dartmoor as 'the sexbed of England'. The hooter was a convenient warning that hubby would soon be home, It was also a signal for the cons to hurl obscene remarks at the screws, which didn't make for friendly relations. One day the use of the hooter for this purpose was stopped, and the sexy ladies of Princetown had to fall back on the old alarm clock.

The evenings on the Moor were anything but rounds of pleasure. For the first eighteen months of his sentence the con was locked up in his cell after tea, and remained there until the following morning. If he had been a good boy, he then went on stageone, and on two nights a week he was allowed to associate with his fellow prisoners for one hour, during which he could play dominoes, darts or draughts. Card games were not permitted. After a further year he went on to stage two, which gave him an extra night on the tiles. The third and final stage was reached after four years, when the prisoner was transferred to D wing and was able to indulge himself for an hour every night, in a wild orgy of dominoes, draughts, darts and, the cherry on life's cocktail, a game of billiards or snooker. He could also have a radio sent in.

The first stage rule was relaxed in my case, and I went on association shortly after I was introduced to the Moor. I also managed to acquire a primitive radio, known as a 'W', on which I was able to get the Home Service. These illegal sets consisted of a diode with a couple of terminals, one of which was earthed, the other attached to the bell-push in the cell. The one I had was made by Donald Hume, who was an electrician on the works party and was doing twelve years for accessory to murder. He was one of the few blokes to get away with murder, and his case made criminal history, since he was acquitted of the capital crime but later, after his release from prison, confessed to a Sunday newspaper that he had in fact killed car-dealer Stanley Setty and distributed his chopped-up body over the Essex marshes.

Hume skipped off to Switzerland, where he committed more crimes. He was sent back to this country and ended up in Broadmoor, where it is a safe bet that he will spend the rest of his life.

I must give a mention to cocoa-time, which came at the end of the prison day when we were banged up for the night. At about seven-thirty the cocoa party made a round of the cells carrying jugs of brown liquid with a film of grease floating on the top. I soon got into the habit of saving the meagre ration of sugar which had been doled out at teatime and adding it to the so-called cocoa, which made it drinkable. This nightcap, so I was told, was heavily laced with bromide to repress the sexual urge. Even the small pleasure of masturbation was made as difficult as possible.

Frequent reference has been made to food in these pages, which is not surprising considering that we were always hungry. We got up to all kinds of dodges to get a bit extra, bribing the kitchen workers with snout for a few pieces of duff and so on and thieving anything edible that was around. But, although the prison authorities point with pride at the menus, claiming that they are varied and adequate, everybody on the staff from the Governor downwards turned a blind eye to the staggering amount of grub that went out of the front gate and turned up in the screws quarters. As he went off duty, each screw would collect his 'parcel' from the kitchen, sugar, tea, a joint of meat, fresh bread, canned goods and anything else that was going. These were looked upon as the perks of the job. Nobody cared that the hungry prisoner was left with the scrag ends of meat, watery tea, insufficient sugar and an unsatisfied appetite.

There was no work at the weekends. It was then that most of the visits took place when relatives and friends travelled from all over the country, spending hours on trains and buses for the doubtful pleasure of spending an hour looking through a sheet of wired glass and talking to the prisoner via a closemeshed grill as a screw patrolled behind him. It must have been shattering for a wife, longing to put her arms round her man, and even worse for the kids wondering why they couldn't touch their dads.

The weekly football match was played on Saturday, an event in which I sometimes took part. If I didn't play, I watched the game, a fiercely contested battle during which many of the cons took the opportunity to pay off old scores. I didn't envy the referee, poor sod, his whistle worked overtime as he did his best to maintain some sort of order. All was not blessed and quiet on the touchlines either as the cons came to blows when violence erupted on the playing field.

Part of the weekend was reserved for God. Attendance at the Sunday service was compulsory, but I doubt that anybody derived spiritual uplift from the dreary sermons droned from the pulpit. The choir was largely composed of fairies, who siezed the chance to wear anything approaching a frock. Dolled up in cassock and surplice, wearing the teeniest trace of make-up, they lent a bizarre touch to this parody of religious observance. Add to this a bunch of the choicest villains in the country singing 'Nearer my God to thee' and you have a sight that beggars the imagination.

I came of age on the Moor in more ways than one. On my twenty-first birthday, alone in my cell, I scribbled the following lines. I don't claim that they are great poetry, but they express what I felt at the time.

> The gift I shall most like
> I shall most certainly not get.
> Others may get the key of the door
> But not if they come of age,
> As I shall, in Dartmoor.
> In Dartmoor they are more careful
> With their keys than that.

The Moor gobbled up five years of my youthful life, and they were very important years. As a raw kid of twenty I was thrown in at the deep end among a ripe collection of some of the most violent and brutal criminals of that era. At the time I didn't realise what might have happened to me, but looking back now, with Wandsworth, Chelmsford and Parkhurst behind me, I am amazed that I came through with only a few scars as witness of those early Dartmoor days.

Some events stand out in my memory. The picture of Bobby Ramsey, ex-boxer and an associate of Billy Hill, serving seven for a bloody attack on Terry Martin in 1956, is as fresh in my mind as though it were yesterday. He had suddenly got religious, and marched round the touchline at the Saturday football game calling on God for help and guidance. It couldn't be anything but a joke.

'Turn it in, Bobby,' said one of the spectators. 'You might kid the chaplain but you can't kid God. He can see through you.'

The angel of light, love and mercy turned on the doubting Thomas and knocked him spark out with a right-hander that spread the poor fellow's nose all over his face. This smiting of the philistine went unnoticed by all but a few of those standing nearby. Perhaps it was even too quick for God to see.

Ramseys conversion didn't last long after that, and it wasn't long before he returned to his former ways. The ex-avenging angel is still knocking people out to this day, but not at God's behest.

While on the matter of religion, the church building deserves a mention. Apart from the Sunday services, it also did duty as cinema, concert hall and general entertainment centre. On these festive occasions the six observation posts, three on either side of the hall, were packed with screws as we watched ancient films such as 'The Perils of Pauline', the original version of 'Bengal Lancers' and similar masterpieces, in numb-arsed boredom.

There were also live concerts at which a few well-known faces put in an appearance, but the other side of the coin was represented by well-intentioned do-gooders who thought that a captive audience would tamely watch any old rubbish. They were soon disillusioned. The Womens' Institute soprano, giving an off-key rendering of Ave Maria, was interrupted by yells of 'Get off, you old strumpet' or 'Show us yer knickers'. The performer at a Moor concert had to be good or the act died the death.

There were times when the church also served as an abattoir. This happened when a certain con was marked down for a bit of treatment by some of his fellows, on account of his having offended against their ideas of what was right and proper. The intended victim would take his seat while the attacker chose a place immediately behind him. The victim would have a couple of the attacker's mates ranged either side of him. When the lights went out the attacker would grab the geezer by the hair, pull his head back and go to work on him with a chiv. Following that performance, which was over in a couple of seconds, the victim would be pushed violently forward over the seats in front while the chiv was thrown as far away as possible.

When the lights went on and the commotion had died down, the injured man would be found some distance from the scene of the attack. When the screws had sorted things out, it was quite likely that several innocents would be nicked for the crime of having blood-stained clothing. It was also more than likely than the real perpetrators would get off scot-free. The authorities were not interested in the finer points of establishing guilt. A man had been cut, you had blood on your clothes therefore you had been concerned in the incident; so down the chokey you go, remanded for the Visiting Magistrates,

The reasons for these cuttings and stabbings were many and various. The victim might be considered a grass, an informer either to the police or the prison authorities. Again, he might have been sentenced for sex offences against young children or crimes of violence against his own kids. But the main reason for these attacks, which resulted in serious maiming and sometimes death, was a row over a few pennyworth of tobacco.

The situation commonly boiled down to this. A prisoner was paid half-a-crown a week, which was just enough to buy three-eighths of an ounce of tobacco, a packet of cigarette papers and a box of matches. By making his roll ups very thin and skilfully splitting each match into four with a needle he would have enough smokes to last him for about four days. The plight of the heavy smoker who had his wages docked for some offence against prison discipline can be imagined. It was then that the miserable con turned to the tobacco baron.

The baron played an important part in the prison economy. Snout was the currency of the cons. Betting on horse races, purchasing favours, bribing the kitchen party for extra food, all these transactions were carried out on the snout exchange. The baron was a man who, via outside contacts and bent screws, was able to build up a store of this valuable commodity and he was a king in the nick, literally having the power of life and death over the other inmates.

This was how it worked in practice. The con would go to baron A and the loan of an ounce of snout to be repaid plus fifty percent interest on the next pay day. Unable to meet the deadline, he would go to baron B and borrow enough snout to cover his original debt. Finally he would end up owing far more than he would be able to repay from his pittance of a wage. He then had two courses open to him. He could apply to the Governor under rule 43 for segregation from other prisoners or he could brazen it out.

The con who chose the latter course of action was on a hiding to nothing. Obviously the Baron could not allow such a liberty as non-payment of the debt, which would undermine his authority in the nick. Thus the defaulter would meet with a serious accident which landed him in hospital or, in some cases, the mortuary. A life for a few bobsworth of snout' seems incredible, doesn't it? Yet in the nick small grievances are magnified out of all proportion.

Jimmy Essex had a bet on with another con, the stake being a portion of dinner time duff. This duff was almost uneatable, but very filling. The debt was not settled, either through forgetfulness or deliberately, and Essex stuck a pair of scissors into the other bloke, who died as a result. The killer had another ten years added to his sentence and the victim was put underground for ever. All this for what amounted to no more than a handful of flour.

I was a non-smoker then, as I am now, but I still managed to get myself involved in a tobacco barons' war between a team of Londoners and a Scottish mob, as a result of which I ended up in hospital with serious cuts to my face and back.

I have often thought about the attitude of the prison authorities to this trafficking in tobacco, and have come to the conclusion that they turned a blind eye to it. They knew who the barons were, and it would be a simple matter to turn them over regularly and confiscate their stock, which would have put them out of business. So why wasn't this done? reckon they thought that, as long as the cons fought each other, they wouldn't be fighting against the system that was the cause of the bother in the first place.

There are two memories of the Moor that will remain engraved on my mind as long as I live. One is that I spent my twenty first birthday banged up in a cold, wet peter. The other is that the news was brought to me that my father had died and I was refused permission to attend the funeral by some snotnose bastard sitting behind a desk at the Home Office.

At last the great day came, the day when I left behind me the dirt, depression and degradation of Dartmoor. I returned to London in style in a Rolls Bentley which had been sent by Bryan Turner, a mate from my schooldays, who was later to cop for twenty-one years for his part in the Ilford and Wembley bank raids, total proceeds three hundred and seventy five thousand pounds.

It's a tradition among the brotherhood of villains that anyone who has been away for a long stretch gets a 'welcome home' party. Mine was a real slap-up affair. Publicans and bookies from the Dale had clubbed together with my brothers and some mates from the manor and taken over a large house in Notting Hill. When I got there, the party was in full swing. Booze was unlimited and there was a fair ration of birds.

It wasn't long before I was feeling on top of the world, what with the drink and the food and all that, so I cast my eyes round for a bit of the other, of which there was plenty available. I captured a right little raver and wasted no time in whipping her outside the room and into the passage. I had intended to make for one of the bedrooms but my feelings got the better of me. She wasn't wearing any knickers, which meant that she was open for the business, so I lifted her dress and got stuck in and it was lovely after all those years of dreaming about it.

I was just about to shoot my load when the door was flung open and what seemed like an army rushed past us. The bird gave a scream, hooked herself off the rod and scarpered. I thought that it was a police raid, and rushed down into the street where a real battle was going on. About a dozen blokes from the party were knocking bags of shit out of a couple of geezers, giving them a proper seeing-to before throwing them into a pile of dustbins. Eventually we all go back indoors, where I find out what has caused the ruck.

It seems that one of the birds was looking out of the window and saw these two blokes messing about with one of the cars, a white Jag which belonged to one of the tastiest villains in the East End.

'Hey, who owns the white Jag outside,' she yells above the tumult going on.

The owner, thinking he has scored, chirped up right away.

'It's mine, darling. Fancy a ride?'

'Not really,' replied the bird, 'but there are two blokes down there who do. They're trying to nick it.'

That's what caused the stampede. I couldn't help but feel sorry for the two poor sods who'd copped for a spanking. They must have been overjoyed when they saw this long line of very expensive motors just waiting to be nicked. Even if it came on top, the worst they could expect was a half-hearted chase by a few flabby company directors. How they must have felt when they were dropped on by a dozen of the most diabolical villains in London can be imagined.

As was usual, the boys had a whip-round for me, so I wasn't short of marching money. The Kray twins had chipped in with a hundred nicker which was very decent of them. I had a few days' holiday during which I saw some old mates and generally picked up the threads of my old life once more.

One day I stumbled across some basement premises in Russell Road, Kensington, part of a house owned by Peter Rachman the slum landlord who had operated in Notting Hill for several years. I got to know him quite well, but our relationship was not to last for he died in November '62. He was mixed up with a couple of birds,

Christine Keeler and Mandy Rice-Davies, who later figured in the Profumo scandal. However, that's by the way. I rented the basement and started a drinker which I called the Basement Club.

I did very well here, and began to scout around for other premises where I could open up. In this type of business it was as well to have several irons in the fire, for the drinkers were illegal and could be closed down at a moment's notice by the police. I came across several suitable premises in the Notting Hill and Holland Park areas, and was soon drawing a steady income from the operation.

From the point of view of the operator, a drinker is a very viable proposition. For a start, the costs are almost negligible, because you don't bother with decoration or any of that nonsense, just run up a makeshift bar and put in a few chairs and tables and keep the lighting down to hide the holes in the carpets and the tattered wallpaper. As for stock, I was on to a good thing with a wholesaler in Princedale Road who allowed me lengthy credit. Furthermore, it was an all-cash affair. We had nothing to do with cheques, not even good ones.

During the period when I was knocking around the estate agents looking for premises, I came across a bloke called Ken Archibald, who was working in one of the offices. Later on he approached me with a proposition. He had left the estate agents and taken a job as resident caretaker of a posh tennis club in Holland Park which was, according to him, an ideal spot for a late - night drinker. As he outlined it, the plan would be to take over the place at eleven and run it until four in the morning as a high-class joint with all mod. cons. Realising that Archibald could well be painting a rosy picture of a wooden tennis hut with a counter and sink, I said I would like to see the place. He took me there that evening.

It was an eye-opener, a large house in its own grounds with lawns and tennis courts and furnished regardless of cost. The carpets were knee-deep, the oak-panelled bar was fully fitted, comfortable leather chairs were scattered around and the full-length curtains were of expensive velvet. Even the toilets were carpeted, and the ladies' boasted a pair of bidets. I couldn't wait to get the place opened.

The first night went with a bang and after that we never looked back. As the word spread, the club became the 'in' place to go for a late drink and, as can be imagined, the clients were a very mixed bag . There were brasses and their ponces rubbing shoulders with villains and well-known figures from the worlds of sport and the arts. I had recruited a pair of very tasty lads to help me keep order, but the customers were allowed to do pretty well what they liked short of breaking up the furniture or otherwise damaging the fixtures and fittings. There was one inflexible rule. At four o'clock in the morning they were all out. Then Archibald and myself, with the aid of a gang of helpers, tidied the place up, replaced the stock we had used and departed.

At odd moments I used to speculate about how the society birds would have felt if they had known that the toilets they used were also serving the needs of some painted old slash-pot, probably dosed up to the eye-balls, and that the very carpet on which they stood had been a rumping-place for a brass while her ponce did a piss in the bidet. There were times also when I had nightmares in case some old dear, returning from an evening at the theatre, would call to pick up a forgotten article and find her tennis club packed with unauthorised members.

There was also the ever-present threat of a police raid for, though we took precautions against noise and always kept the curtains tightly drawn, there was considerable coming and going which must have attracted the attention of neighbouring householders. A raid would have put the kybosh on the whole enterprise, since the usual practice was for the Old Bill to take the names and addresses of the customers, arrest the person in charge of the bar and impound the stock. Lady Luck must have been on our side on that score. We had no aggravation from the forces of law and order.

One of the regular punters who I got to know very well was ex-world champion boxer Freddie Mills, who would often drop in for a drink in the early hours. He was later to die in mysterious circumstances, being found outside his West End club in a car with a .22 rifle by his side and a gunshot wound in the head. The coroner's verdict was that he committed suicide, but my view, which is shared by his widow and many others, is that Freddie was the victim of gangland murder.

Another regular was actor Paul Carpenter, a jovial boozer who could always be relied upon to be the life and soul of the party until he fell down. One night he passed out on one of the settees, and a couple of brasses got out his penis, drew a ring round it with a lipstick and replaced it. It was all good, clean fun.

In the main the punters behaved themselves, but sooner or later a row was bound to break out, an event which happened after the club had been running for just over two months. The Mills brothers, a pair of villains out of Notting Hill and no relation to Freddie, had a ruck with a bloke who had upset them. They dragged this fellow into the women's' loo and set about him. When I arrived on the scene along with my helpers the damage had been done, with the victim on the carpet in an unconscious condition, mirrors smashed and blood all over the floor and walls.

The first thing to be done was to clear the premises, which wasn't difficult. I announced that we were about to be raided and asked the punters to leave as quickly and quietly as possible. As soon as they had left I set about trying to sort it all out. The Mills brothers got their marching orders and left without any further trouble, while one of my helpers took the injured man to hospital in his cab. There was no way, however, in which we could repair the damage to the toilet in the time at our disposal, so that was the end of our late-night drinker, which was a pity.

I gathered my stocks of booze together and departed. Archibald promised that he would make up some story about vandals breaking into the club, the damage would anyway be covered by insurance and so we were all in the clear. So I thought, but I reckoned without Archibald, who later turned out to be a very unreliable character indeed.

Shortly after the Holland Park drinker had gone up the spout I was approached by a little firm from the West End who owned an hotel in Pembridge Gardens, This gaff had been run by a chap called Serge Paplinski, a sort of adopted son of Peter Rachman, who had allowed it to get into a run down state, but the firm who took it over had tarted it up and filled half the fifty rooms with brasses.

Tarts and trouble go together, as the hotel's new owners quickly found out. Their proposition was that I should mind the place, in return for which I would have my own flat and a handsome earner, and it would be up to me to use my own methods to keep the peace. It was an offer I couldn't refuse. I moved into the flat, which was nicely furnished and very comfortable, and settled down to enjoy myself.

The work wasn't hard and I had plenty of time on my hands, so that I was able to keep an eye on my other club interests. I was still involved with the Basement Club in Russell Road, which I visited frequently, and I also had other irons in the fire. However, I spent a lot of time at the hotel, where I was on good terms with some of the younger brasses who had just started off on the game and weren't all that shop-soiled. If one of them fancied a bit on the side I duly obliged her. It was what I called my 'fucking perks'.

The head girl in this establishment for naughty ladies called herself Annie Laurie. She was a right hard case and knew all the tricks of the trade. She came from Australia and was a great favourite with the lads from down under, who nicknamed her 'The Witch'. I wasn't on very good terms with her on account of the fact that she knew about my encounters with some of her girls. A strict moralist, she didn't approve of them doing it for nothing. I remember one evening I was standing in the foyer when one of the girls came in with a punter, a well-dressed geezer carrying a briefcase. Annie stepped forward.

'Good evening, sir,' she said. 'One moment, I'll have your case taken care of.'

She turned to me and snapped her fingers. 'Porter. Take this gentleman's case up.'

I didn't know whether to laugh or belt her one. Anyway, I copped for the case and led the way upstairs, then nipped back sharpish to have a ruck with the saucy cow. Needless to say, she had done a disappearing act.

The basement part of the building was a club, all legal and above-board, run by Jeanette Roberts and her husband Roland. His real name was Kofi, and he was press Attaché to the Ghana High Commission. He was a very well-educated man and spoke several languages, and it was due to him that the Garden Club, as it was known, numbered among its members three Ambassadors and an assorted bunch of foreign diplomats.

I spent a lot of my time in the club and was on good terms with Roland, who came to rely on me to a great extent in keeping the premises free of trouble. There wasn't a lot of it, since the punters were on the whole a well-behaved lot, but if the clouds began to gather, Roland would give me the signal by stroking the back of one hand with the other and I would sort out the offender, ease him out of the door and attend to him in the yard. On these occasions I was always on to a good drink. Roland ran into trouble later in 1965, when he collected some unfavourable publicity and was recalled to Ghana. Two years afterwards he was nicked, along with a wealthy young Lebanese called Kazoun, and sentenced to four years at the Old Bailey for possessing cannabis.

Meanwhile I was doing very nicely at Pembridge Gardens and money was rolling in from the drinkers in which I had a share. I made some good friends on the way to prosperity.

CHAPTER SIX

ELLEN:

My Aunt Kit was a wise old lady who had a great influence on me while I was growing up. She was the one who told me to hang on to Joe when a lot of people were advising me to give him up as a bad job. She was in a way a very simple person, and that doesn't mean simple-minded. It was just that she followed a few basic rules all her life, and she was none the worse for that.

She was forever on at me about what she called the three L's. Look, listen and learn she would say and I took heed of that when I was carted along to the clubs by Joe and introduced to the people he was associated with. They were so-called gangsters whose names were household words throughout the country. I met Jack Spot at the Miramar club, also his very beautiful wife Rita. Spot was a nickname. His real name was Comer and he was a well-dressed fellow who looked more like a bank manager than a notorious villain. There was a lot of gossip about him being battling with Billy Hill for control of London's underworld. He didn't pay much attention to me. After all I was just Joe Cannon's girl, and as such didn't rate very highly in a gangster's world. That didn't bother me, I looked, listened and learned and kept my mouth shut.

As I saw it these people lived in a world of their own, making their own rules and sticking by them. It was a world where violence was very much to the fore and arguments were settled by brute force. If somebody stepped out of line he was punished very severely, and I don't mean that he received a slap on the wrist. Guns, knives and iron bars took the place of words and serious injury was a commonplace. There were times when the victim of this violence was carried off to the mortuary rather than the hospital. On these occasions the police met with a wall of silence. Nobody knew anything.

As can well be imagined I was concerned about my Joe. He was up to his neck in these shenanigans. He never went anywhere without a shooter stuck in the waistband of his trousers and as everybody knows, a bullet is no respecter of persons. Tough as Joe was, and he was a very hard man indeed, all the muscle in the world can be discounted by a gun in the hands of an idiot who doesn't know what he's doing. There was always in the back of my mind the old saying that if you carry a gun one day you will use it. In those days there were a lot of guns around, some of them in the possession of men who shouldn't have been allowed to carry anything more dangerous than a pocket knife. These were the ones to beware of.

I didn't nag Joe about the risks he might be taking. In his world a nagging woman is, like a toothache, something to be rid of as quickly as possible. There was one occasion, however, when I really let rip. So did his mother. We were both there at the Cannon home when Joe almost fell through the door. His head was a mass of bandages and what could be seen of his face was as white as a sheet. He didn't offer any explanation nor did he reply when we both had a go at him. I learned later that he had been attacked in a club in Knightsbridge by a bunch of gangsters from South London armed with choppers, knives and iron bars. It was a wonder that he wasn't killed.

He made light of it. For a few days he stayed indoors

as the wounds healed. He didn't go back to the hospital where he had been patched up but took the stitches out himself. The scars that remained faded over the next few weeks but remnants of them are still visible.

I was having lots of trouble at home about this time. My dad was back again after his release and was finding it hard to get a regular job. With a large family to support he had to take anything that came along. He did his best but it wasn't really good enough and he and my mum were constantly rowing, which made for an uncomfortable atmosphere. I escaped most of it during the week as I was out at work, but weekends were a bind. I spent much of my time at the Cannon's, where I was always welcome. I didn't see much of Joe. A minder doesn't have a lot of free time to spend on socialising, but we did go out on the town from time to time.

It was on one of these evenings that Joe had a lucky escape. We were having dinner together at a restaurant in Paddington. Joe had a meet with Jack Spot later on, but we were having a good time and he decided to scrub it. It was just as well that he did, because it was the night when Jack was attacked by a half-dozen of Billy Hill's gang and beaten up within an inch of his life. If Joe had been there he would have got some of the same treatment. He might have been killed. The men who took part in the attack were among the toughest villains in the underworld. Mad Frankie Fraser, Bobby Warren and Billy Boy Blythe were known and feared, but Jack Spot's wife put the finger on them and they were sent down for their part in the affray.

I've said before that the menfolk in the Dale didn't take their women into their confidence. It was a tradition, a sort of macho thing that was accepted behaviour. The women didn't prance around burning their bras and yelling slogans, they just got on with their job of keeping the home fires burnlng and looking after the kids. Still, they remained persons in their own right and could be as tough as any man when it came to standing up for what they believed to be their rights. The outstanding villains had outstanding women behind them who did not stand for any nonsense from the authorities. The police understood the situation and played the game according to the rules. There were some inexperienced young coppers who tried it on, questioning the women about the doings of their men, but they soon learned that they were on a hiding to nothing.

One woman I remember particularly. Her man was not an outstanding villain, just an ordinary thief of which there were many on the manor. He was always in trouble and rarely a day passed that there was a uniform knocking on her door. She had five or six kids who were following in their father's footsteps, nicking anything they could lay their hands on. A performance that was repeated every time the law paid a call went something like this. The copper would knock loudly on the door, there would be no reply so he would continue knocking. Finally the door would be opened and the woman would stand on the doorstep.

The conversation was very short.

'I'd like to speak to your husband.' This from the officer.

The woman replies in two words. 'Piss off.'

They both stand staring at each other and getting nowhere. The copper shakes his head and walks away. The woman calls after him in a voice that can be heard for miles.   'Don't bloody-well come back.'

That was the state of affairs and the law accepted it. In their view there were more ways of killing a pig than slitting its throat and there would always be another day. It was a war in which both sides won occasional victories, but it was never-ending.

So far as my home life was concerned things were getting on top of me. I was the only regular wage earner in the family. My dad was pretty well unemployable but I will say this for him, he did his best in the circumstances which were very trying indeed. It was only natural that I spent less and less time at home and more time with the Cannon family. I began to think seriously about breaking away and getting a place of my own where Joe and I could set up house together and have a chance of spending time alone whenever possible. For the time being it was a dream, but I made it come true later.

I remember very clearly one day when I read in the paper about a wages snatch at a dairy in St. John's Wood. I hadn't seen Joe for several days before that and I somehow suspected that he had a hand in the robbery. It turned out that I had guessed right because shortly afterwards he was nicked along with a couple of his mates. There was the usual remand in custody but there was no doubt about the outcome. I was at the Old Bailey when Joe was sent down for seven years for his part in the affair. He got the longest sentence of the five of them because he had coshed one of the wages clerks with what the prosecution alleged was the butt of a gun. As can well be imagined we were both in a state of shock. Joe had lost his freedom and I had lost my man and our future, for the next years, looked very bleak. In the cells below the Old Bailey I saw him briefly and he did his best to console me. For my part I told him that I would be waiting for him when he came out. I must say Joe took it very well, he was almost cheerful as we said goodbye to each other. He even said 'see you soon', which I thought was peculiar in the circumstances. I had the disturbing thought in the back of my mind that he was already thinking about going over the wall. He wasn't the sort who would take kindly to the prospect of being banged up in a cell for a few months, let alone several years.

So there I was, a nineteen-year-old girl, feeling very much on my own though I did not lack for caring relatives and friends. Aunt Kit was, as usual, a tower of strength and the Cannon family rallied round. I didn't get a lot of sympathy at home. They had enough of their own troubles to cope with.

I was shortly to find that I would have need of support. Barely a month after Joe had been sent down I discovered that I was pregnant.

CHAPTER SEVEN

JOE:

In the spring of 1964 I had a lot on my mind. Though I took no part in that caper of all time, the Great Train Robbery of August 1963, the activity on the part of the Old Bill had an effect on all of us who had something to hide. Over two and a half million sobs had gone missing, and that had to be recovered, and there had been interference with Her Majesty's Mail, an offence slightly less serious than interfering with HM herself. The Old Bill had put themselves about, and the waves they made were felt throughout the British Isles.

In the upshot Scotland Yard's Detective Chief Superintendent Tommy Butler led the team that captured practically all of the mob and they were now being weighed off at Aylesbury, with Mr, Justice Edmund Davies in charge of dishing out the porridge. The leading members of the gang copped for thirty years each, a result which sent shivers down the spine of every villain in the country.

I was on nodding terms with Bobby Welch, Charlie Wilson and Ron Biggs, and I later met Tommy Wisbey when I was on the same landing at Hull. I also had several chats with Bruce Reynolds, the leader of the gang, when I was in Parkhurst with him after he had been nicked and sentenced. From what I could gather, they were very unlucky not to get away with it.

There has been plenty of newspaper comment on this job, and books have been written airing all kinds of theories about the master-mind who set it up. I have my own ideas about that. There is a man who must be nameless who had the contacts and the organising ability to do it. He wasn't among those who got away, because he was never there. I'm not the only man who knows his name, but I have yet to meet anybody who has the guts to publish it. One day, after a famous funeral, the truth will be told.

The news of the sentences awarded to the train robbers forced another story out of the headlines. This one was very local and I was to become deeply involved. While I was running the illegal drinker at the Holland Park Tennis Club, I heard that one of the brasses from the Notting Hill area had been found murdered by the Thames at Chiswick, not far from a pub called the Windmill. Her name was Irene Lockwood, but she was also known as Sandra Russell, She had been to the club a few times, although I discouraged her, because she was as ugly as sin and stank like a polecat.

Her nude body was found by the river police in the early hours of the morning of the 8th of April, She was quickly identified and the Old Bill turned over her drum that same day. Among her belongings they found a card on which was the name Kenny and the telephone number of the Tennis Club. Kenny was, of course, Kenny Archibald the caretaker. The Old Bill had him in the nick for questioning in double-quick time. Now I was well and truly in the shit. Archibald had only to mention my name and I would be up to my neck in a murder enquiry.

I claimed the man as he left the nick and steered him into the Mitre, a boozer on the other side of Ladbroke Grove.

'Alright, Kenny, let's have it and no bullshit,' I said. 'What did you say to the law?'

The poor geezer was terrified. 'I didn't say anything about you, Joe,' he said. 'I just told them I had the cards printed for private parties in my flat when they asked me, I wasn't in there long.' That was the truth. I knew that he had only been in the station for half-an-hour. I also knew from experience that most of the time he would have been left to sweat it out in the interview room.

'You still at the Tennis Club?' I asked.

'Yes.' 'Right,' I said. 'Let me know if they sort you out again. And keep your mouth shut. Understand?'

He understood. I let him go on his way, but I still felt uneasy. He was no villain, and if the Old Bill leaned on him he was a dead cert to crack under pressure. However, there was nothing I could do about it. I discussed the situation with Reggie Short, a good mate who had helped me at the Tennis Club, and we decided that the best thing I could do was to make myself scarce for a while. Reggie drove me down to Brighton in his cab, and I booked in at Cook's Hotel, a small but comfortable gaff where my comings and goings wouldn't attract too much interest.

I stayed there a few days and talked on the telephone with Reggie every morning. Not being the sort of bloke who enjoys sitting around doing nothing I wasn't all that happy, and when Reggie informed me that there were no signs that the Old Bill were after me but that some of the bold boys were taking liberties in my clubs, I had it back to London at the double. I did a tour of the clubs that same evening, in the course of which I straightened out a few characters, and things were soon back to normal.

For some reason which I couldn't work out, the enquires into the murder seemed to have shifted away from Notting Hill. I got a whisper that the Old Bill were very active in the Lockwood women's home town, which was fine by me. The cow had been nothing but a nuisance when she was alive. Now that she was dead, she was best forgotten. One thing the Lockwood affair did was to bring me and Reggie more into each other's company. Actually I liked old Reg a lot. We had been at school together and, although he was two years older than me, we had much in common. He was a very good boxer, and I reckon he could have been a championship contender in the heavyweight division when he grew up. Standing over six feet and weighing in at something like fifteen stone, he was a good man to have on your side in a battle.

He had started off in life as a butcher's apprentice, and he was carving up carcases in the Dale when I was punching heads in at Portland Borstal, Later on he chucked the butchering lark, took his knowledge and became a licensed cabbie. We had kept in touch even during the time I was away in Dartmoor, and we saw quite a bit of each other when I was at home.

He was good fun at a party, laughing and joking and doing his impressions of famous people, particularly Schnozzle Durante and Humphrey Bogart, which brought the house down. When I started up in the club business he often dropped in to see me and have a chat, in fact he spent so much of his time doing this that I suggested we put his visits on a permanent and paying basis. He could do the odd bit of door-minding when he wasn't driving. It was also useful to have a legal cab on call for the punters. It turned out a very successful arrangement, and he certainly made more money than he would have done merely tooling round the streets picking up fares.

The situation at the time when Lockwood met her violent end was very chaotic business-wise. There had been the rumpus at the Tennis Club, which put paid to a first-class money spinner, and my short holiday in

Brighton had encouraged some of the little firms to move in on my territory, so I was constantly having aggravation. I dealt with it, but it took time and energy. The truth of the matter is that I had too much on my plate but wouldn't admit it.

The Old Bill were an ever-present threat. I was known to them because of my previous form, and they kept a watch on me, ready to pounce if I stepped out of line. Reggie was a great help to me, as he was able to provide the means of transport from club to club. To use a car registered in my name would have been stupid. We both developed eyes in the backs of our heads, and I can tell you we needed them. In the minds of both of us was the knowledge that, if Kenny Archibald grassed, we would both be in trouble.

Another cause for worry was the brasses, who were screaming their heads off to the Old Bill. I couldn't bar them from the clubs, where they always had the right to pick up punters, for that would have caused a riot. All I could do was accept them as a necessary evil, and evil was the right word to describe them.

Now I'm no moralist, but I never reckoned brasses deserved much consideration. There must have been something wrong with them in the upstairs department for them to go on the game in the first place. When you consider that they're ready to take on ten different men in a night, some of them poxed-up, it makes you wonder what goes on in their minds. From what I know of them they are unscrupulous, unpredictable, unreasonable and without a shred of conscience. Most of them are into petty thieving and wherever they go it's trouble.

The above remarks apply to the slags at the bottom end of the market who charge a few pounds for a knee-trembler against a wall, a blow-job in the back of a car or a short time on the turf in a public park. There are high-class whores who charge the earth, are choosy about the clients they take on and are an entirely different proposition. I never needed to use any of them in the way of trade. I had no difficulty in getting all the nooky I wanted without paying for it.

The owner of a drinker, as I have mentioned, couldn't keep the brasses out because they were part of the service, so to speak. In the dim lighting, even an old slash-pot looked attractive to a bloke with a skinful of booze, and the punters expected to be able to pick up a quick fuck for a few sobs. I have often been amazed to see quite respectable-looking blokes nip outside for a short time with some raddled old bag who they wouldn't normally have given the time of day.

There is a pretty sick story which I think tells it all. A couple of brasses were walking down the Bayswater Road Blimey, says one to the other, my fanny don't 'arf itch. Why don't you scratch it, says her mate. Scratch it? I wouldn't touch it with a barge-pole, replied the complainer.

Joking apart, having these quarrelsome cows in a drinker was like sitting on a keg of dynamite, and somebody had to be there to control any situation that looked like getting out of hand. This is where Reggie came in useful. He had the knack of being able turn a tense moment into a laughing matter with a few words at the right time. If, in spite of his amiable approach, there seemed no way of avoiding a row, people thought twice about tackling this friendly giant with the flattened hooter. If a full-scale ruck developed, Reggie was capable of settling it single-handed

Normally Reggie drank and joked with the brasses but at times when, for no apparent reason, he would sort one of them out for a bit of treatment, he would be anything but friendly. It would start off with a few whispered remarks accompanied by some painful pinching.

One of the brasses had the sauce to complain to me, but it didn't get her anywhere. I told her that she could stay away from the joint if she didn't like the conditions. She then persuaded her ponce to have a pop at Reggie, which got neither of them anywhere. Reggie beat the ponce to a pulp, kicked the slag senseless and warned them both off the manor.

It rather puzzled me when I thought about it. He was a straight fellow with no criminal record, but he seemed to relish being mixed up with the shady world of drinkers and the people who used them. He took care of his mother, with whom he lived in a flat in Hammersmith. My thinking led to no real conclusion except that it takes all kinds to make a world and Reggie fitted in somewhere or other.

About a week after I came back from Brighton another murder hit the headlines. The nude body of a woman had been found about a mile away from the spot where Irene Lockwood's corpse had been discovered. The papers named her as Helene Barthelemy, but I knew her as a whore who called herself Helene Thompson, She was well-known at the Jazz Club in Westbourne Road
a gaff which catered for West Indians and was run by a chap known as African Peter. I had a small share in this place, and visited it quite frequently. She had also come to the Tennis Club on a few occasions. According to reports she was a good performer who made no secret of the fact that she fancied blacks.

The press went to town on this second Jack the Ripper type killing, describing in detail the last night of her life, how she danced and drank at the Jazz Club into the early hours of the morning, climbing the steps that led to Westbourne Road and stepping out into the dawn, never to be seen alive again. This was on the morning of the 22nd of April, Medical evidence showed that she had been dead for forty-eight hours when her naked body was found five miles from the scene of her last dance.

Having got nowhere with the Lockwood case, the Old Bill really put themselves about on this one. They ran a fine dragnet over the manor, pulling in a large proportion of the West Indians for questioning and poking their noses into every criminal nook and cranny. One night they raided the Basement Club while I was there and found a stolen one-armed bandit on the premises. They came the heavy with me, and I ended up chinning one of them, with the result that I was nicked for receiving and assault and also lost the club, which was closed down.

It looked as though everything was coming on top, so my feelings could be imagined when I heard that Archibald had walked into the nick and confessed to the murder of Irene Lockwood. This was a facer. The idiot had lost any bottle he ever had, and it was odds on that he would cough the lot, in which case I would be in the frame as a suspect in both murders, for it was obvious that Archibald had made a false confession. He wasn't capable of killing a fly.

I had no option but to get off the manor, but I wanted to be near the scene of the action. One of Reggie's mates had a flat in Soho, and I holed up there. I kept in touch with what was going on in Notting Hill through Reggie. Cabbies, like postmen and milkmen, are anonymous. They can come and go without attracting any special attention.

Reggie attended the hearing at Acton magistrates

court when Archibald pleaded not guilty to a charge of murder and was committed to the Old Bailey for trial. I also learned that he had blown the whistle on the set-up at the Tennis Club, putting my name up as the organiser. The Old Bill had got the message and were out looking for me. It was all bad news.

There was nothing for it but to sit tight and let things take their course. In the meantime I had a living to earn. Ronnie and Reggie Kray were by now well-established in the West End, and they were able to put quite a bit of work my way. The Nash brothers, who were minding the Bagatelle in Cork Street, also steered me towards a few earners. Very soon I was doing better financially than I had ever done with the drinkers, which was some consolation. The press had now started to refer to the killings of Lockwood and Thompson as the Nude Murders, but they couldn't comment on them in any detail because Archibald was due to appear at the Old Bailey at the end of June. It was a cock-eyed situation. Archibald had confessed to killing the Lockwood woman, then pleaded not guilty at the magistrates' court. Everybody knew that the miserable bastard was as innocent as a new-born babe, but the law had to take its course. Archibald duly appeared up the steps at the Bailey, was duly acquitted and promptly took off for parts unknown.

Three weeks later the nude body of a woman was found on the forecourt of a garage in Berrymede Road, a cul-de-sac off Acton Lane, which was three miles away from where the bodies of the other two murdered women had been discovered. In life she had been Mary Fleming, alias Mary Turner, a brass from Notting Hill who had been known to me as a frequent visitor to both the Jazz Club and the Tennis Club.

The press had a field day over this new development,

and naturally the Old Bill had to take quite a bit of stick, which didn't please the top brass at the Yard. At the same time as one of the sensational Sundays implored the killer to give himself up, orders went out to step up the hunt. It was very nearly impossible to move in Notting Hill without bumping into a copper. I kept my head down in Soho while the faithful Reggie brought me news of the happenings on my home manor. It was now certain that I was in the frame as a prime suspect the enquiry, for the Old Bill had visited my home, questioned my relatives and friends and made it plain that they wanted to get their hands on me.

Although I was only a few miles from the area, I felt reasonably safe. In theory communications between the various divisions of the Met were good, but in practice they didn't work out all that well. The Regional Crime Squads that had just been organised were having teething troubles in the early stages, a fact well known to all the villains. I didn't stick myself up as a target, but I did take precautions against having my collar felt and they worked.

Meanwhile the press had been doing some simple arithmetic after chasing up unsolved murders in the West London districts. Elizabeth Figg was a prostitute. She was found dead on the river bank at Dukes' Meadows near Chiswick Bridge on the 17th June, 1959. The partly decomposed body of another brass, Gwyneth Rees, was uncovered by workmen on a patch of waste ground in Mortlake on November 8th, 1963. There was another unsolved case, Hannah Tailford, found dead beside the Thames in January 1964. A grand total of six murders, all of which might have been committed by the same killer'

It never rains but it pours. On August 12th 1964, Charlie Wilson,one of the train robbers, strolled out of

Birmingham's Winson Green jail. Somehow the whisper got around that I was one of the gang who helped him to escape, and that Charlie had been whipped off to some secret place, tortured until he revealed where he had stashed his share of the loot and then killed. In fact Charlie made his getaway to Canada and was at liberty for over three years.

The newshounds of the popular press were not slow to pick up this hot story. One of them claimed me one night in the Bagatelle, and made no secret of his intention to stick with me until I had revealed all. That I had nothing to reveal was neither here nor there. To cut a long story short, I was chased all over London and parts of Kent until I managed to give them the slip and have it away to Brighton and Cook's Hotel.

Reggie drove me to Brighton in his cab. We arrived on a fine August evening and sat down in a quiet corner of the bar at Cook's for a drink and a chat. For a while nothing was said. Reggie, who normally rabbited away twenty to the dozen, just sat there staring into his glass as though he was hypnotised.

"Something the matter, Reggie?' I asked.

He was silent for a while, then he took a hefty swig at his drink.

'Did you know that they're saying on the manor that you topped those brasses and I helped you?' he said.

. A statement like that, coming right out of the blue, was like being hit across the nose with a pickaxe handle. 'For fuck's sake, Reggie,' I said. 'You know that's not my line.'

'Sure, Joe,' he said. 'I know that. So do you. But what about the others? That bloody Archibald.....'

We both knew what he was talking about. Kenny had

dropped me right in it with the law, who were looking for a convenient body. With my form there was every possibility that I could be fitted up.

'So what do we do?' I said.

'There's only one thing for it. You'll have to keep out of the way till the heat's off. I'll go back to London and keep in touch with you on the blower.

I couldn't think of anything else, so we had to leave it like that. Reggie left, and I went up to my room with a bottle of Scotch. I had plenty to think about. Was Reggie telling me the truth? Or did he know more than he was letting on to? I remembered the look on his face when he threw the slut Lockwood out of the Tennis Club, and wondered if the incident had ended there.

When I was nicked the following day in the lounge of the hotel I kept my mouth shut. The two bogeys were very affable and chatted freely as they drove me to London. Even John du Rose then a Detective Chief Superintendent on the Murder Squad was very pleasant when I was marched into his office at New Scotland Yard. I wasn't kidded. I'd been verballed before by experts, so I knew the score.

In my dealings with the Old Bill I had always put on an air of helpless stupidity, but willing to be helpful. I don't think du Rose fell for it, but the game was played according to the rules. He offered me a cigarette, which I refused, explaining that I was a non-smoker.

'Now, Joey,' he began, 'what's this about helping Charlie Wilson to have it away?'

'Nothing to do with me, guv,' I said. I knew the technique. Tackle Chummy about something which he couldn't have done, let him off the hook then swing in with the real stuff while he's patting himself on the back.

'I see. Well, we do know that you couldn't have had

anything to do with it. But you were mixed up with something else, weren't you? Something more serious.'

Hello, I thought, here it comes, the Nude Murders and I wasn't wrong. He went to work on me with question after question to which I must have given the right answers, because he finally gave it up as a bad job.

'Right, Joey,' he said. 'You're going over to Notting Hill. They want to see you there. Good luck.'

On my own manor I knew how to perform. I knew they would think twice about doing me for the illegal drinkers, which meant a lot of paperwork for the Old Bill and no more than a fine on conviction. I was right on that one. I walked out of the nick without any further stains on my character, and lost no time in seeing Reggie and giving him the good news.

I found it curious that Reggie displayed no great joy when I told him that we were off the hook, but I put it down to his sense of relief that left him at a loss for words. All the same, I was conscious of a barrier between us that had not been there before. I had to give up the illegal drinker lark and we saw less and less of each other. Our association ended for good when he died in 1975 in Ashford Hospital. He was only forty years old.

On the 25th of November, 1964, the naked body of a woman was discovered on a patch of waste ground in Horton Street just Off Kensington High Street. She had been dead for some time. She was identified as Margaret McGowan a prostitute from the Bayswater area.

On the 16th of February, 1965, the naked body of a woman was found in an alley in Acton, West London. She was Bridget O'Hara, a prostitute who had plied her trade in Shepherd's Bush Hammersmith, Notting Hill and Bayswater.

Over the years I have often thought about the strange

affair in which I was involved. Were these killings the work of one man who followed the same pattern each time~ Was he a modern Jack the Ripper, who stalked the gaslit streets of Edwardian London, leaving behind him a trail of dead whores? Was he, like Peter Sutcliffe, known as the Yorkshire Ripper, a man driven by an obsessive urge to slay women of easy virtue? Or was there more than one killer? If so, where are they? The fact remains that no one, as yet, has been convicted of these crimes. The file is still open.

Every villain I know has a 'one that got away' story. Knowing how luck plays an important part in any blag, many of them must be true. This one is the real McCoy.

A couple of pals brought me some genuine information about a diamond merchant's in Hatton Garden which is, by the way, one of the best-policed streets in London. Burglar alarm technology in the early sixties was not what it is today, but some trust was placed in security guards. They, being human, often fell by the way, and this particular geezer who was on duty in the building was prepared to leave the premises unguarded for an hour for a cash consideration.

We had to have a good peterman or safe-blower for the job, because the diamonds were stored in an old Milner. One of my mates brought in The Professor - he was really known by that name - and the four of us set out one night to do the job. We met in a pub just off Hatton Garden and had a couple of drinks as we waited for the nod from the security guard.

The guard turns up on the dot, comes into the pub and tips us the wink that we can go to work. We have one hour. We go over to the office building, enter by the main door and go up to the third floor. There is enough light coming in from the street so we don't need torches. John is on the stairs where he can see the street through a window.

Me and the Professor go into the office where there is a large safe all on its own in a corner. The Professor gives it the once-over, says it will be no trouble and sets about packing explosive round the lock. I am wandering about in the office, which is also a small workroom, collecting anything lying on the workbenches. Finally the Professor has finished. He sets the detonator and runs the wires out into the passage while I take up the carpet and drape it over the safe and then open the windows so that the blast doesn't blow them out. We get the all clear from John on the stairs and the Professor touches the wires to the terminal of the battery, there is a dull thud and the office fills with smoke.

We go into action. While I close the windows to prevent the tell-tale smoke from drifting out into Hatton Garden, the Professor is tugging away at the door of the safe which has opened a little way and then jammed. According to the Prof another charge is needed, so we repeat the process. The door remains stuck in the same position. I try to squeeze my arm inside to get at the contents but the gap is too small. There is no more jelly and our hour is almost up.

We give the safe a few hefty kicks but without result, and finally have to leave before the guard gets back. The total haul goes to the dabbler for a couple of grand, we have risked a ten stretch for five hundred apiece. Our feelings can be imagined when we read in the mid-day paper that the office cleaner came in, pulled at the door of the safe - and it opened. There was only a quarter of a million quids worth of diamonds in it. To say that we were choked is putting it mildly.

Mind you, not all my operations were a piece of cake. There is a darker side to the underworld of which the public knows nothing. There, violence is a commonplace as teams of villains carve each other up over some incident or other which might seem unimportant to the outside observer. Few of these affrays come before the courts unless a grass informs the Old Bill.

The professional criminal regards the grass as the lowest form of animal life, and every man's hand is against him or her. Whatever the rights or wrongs of a dispute, it should be settled without turning to the law, either by a straightener or a battle between the two sides.

Jack Spot's wife Rita was looked upon as a grass since she had been directly responsible for Frankie Fraser and Bobby Warren being put away, so when she walked into the Magic Carpet club in Shepherd's Bush with a villain called Jimmy Emmett there was some resentment felt that she had been let in. I was one of those who said that the team who owned the club had been out of order, and they got the needle. Out of this single incident came a row that ended with the complete destruction of the Magic Carpet and another club owned by the same team.

What happened was that the Shepherd's Bush mob sorted out a couple of my mates and knocked them about pretty badly to give me the message that they didn't like my attitude in the Rita Comer business. If I hadn't done something about this by way of retaliation my name would have been mud on that manor, and I couldn't afford that. I got a team together, and one evening we dropped in on both clubs and wrecked them. They never re-opened.

The thing about violence is that once it starts it spreads rapidly. You have a ruck with somebody and they can't get back at you so they have a go at somebody who's close, like a mate or one of your family. My brother Tommy was out one night with his wife, having a drink in a local pub. It was a small place with an outside toilet. Tommy went for a slash, but no sooner was he outside the door than four blokes jumped out of a parked car and set about him with knifes, coshes and razors. They cut him up badly, slicing off part of an ear and stabbing him in the body, then they got back in the car and had it away. So far as they were concerned, Tommy could have been a goner.

My brother didn't die, but he was marked for life. He had, however, recognised one of the mob, and rough justice was done a few nights later. In the dead of night two blokes got into this geezer's house and, while one of them held him down on the bed, the other went to work on him with a chiv, giving him all that Tommy received and a bonus. Without going into detail, it would be a miracle if he ever fathered kids.

Perhaps the most frightening aspect of violence is the use of shooters. As a trained boxer I could take care of myself in a punch-up, because I knew how and where to hit. The other fellow also knew this, so if he was fronting me single-handed he would provide himself with a gun. Now, since you can't explain the Queensberry rules to a bullet, and a pair of fists is no match for a .45, I was forced to carry a shooter myself. There's also another side to the question. The finest fighter in the world is no match for a mob armed with knifes and coshes.

A shooter is an excellent weapon of offence or defence, but carrying has its dangers. For starters, if you happen to be carrying and you get nicked, it's a cert that five years will be added to your sentence whatever else happens. I was lucky when I was nabbed in Shepherd's Bush, but if I'd been older I reckon they would have thrown the book at me. Ronnie Kray was also one of the fortunate ones when he made one with Bobby

Ramsey and Billie Jones in '56. He was carrying, but he got away with three years.

There is also the hazard of accidental discharge. Noller Knowles, a mate of mine, carried a shooter which, unknown to him, had a faulty safety catch. He was fishing for his keys outside his own front door when he touched the trigger of the gun. The bullet went straight through his chest, killing him instantly.

Going back to boxing, we were a real fighting family. Even Mum could perform with the best of them, as she proved on one occasion . My brother Nobby was at a party with Yocker Robinson when some woman got the needle and smashed a bottle over Nobby ' s head . Naturally he could not retaliate in kind, but he popped off home and, while Mum attended to his wounds, he told her what had happened. Nothing would satisfy Mum but that this female should get her deserts, so when the doctoring was finished, she piled into Yockers car along with Nobby and they went back to the party.

When they arrived Mum sorted out the woman and squared up to her, giving the surprised female a right whacking, left jabs and right crosses, the whole business, finishing the job by knocking her out with a right hook of which Cassius Clay would not have been ashamed. There the matter would have ended, but this cow nicked Mum, who was bound over to keep the peace at West London. This put an end to Mum's boxing career which, according to Nobby and Yocker, who had ringside seats, was a pity. She showed championship potential.

In the sort of life that I led it doesn't do to be taken by surprise. There's always the possibility of being almost axed in half, cut to ribbons or shot at: so, in any uncertain situation, it's best to take immediate action and leave the apologies until later. For example, I was walking along King Street, Hammersmith, one day when I noticed a bloke coming towards me and giving me the once-over. As we were passing each other he shot out a hand and grabbed me by the arm, mumbling something which I didn't quite hear. My instant reaction was to swing round, bring my knee up sharply into his balls, put a right-hander into his chops and tear his hand away from my arm. Leaving him groaning on the pavement, I had it away.

I thought I had foiled just another villain-inspired attack, but this was not the case. The 'villain' was a plain-clothes Old Bill, and I was done for assault and resisting arrest. There is a little bit of justice left in the world, however, because when I explained the copper's method of arrest, the beak gave me the benefit of the doubt and put me on probation.

CHAPTER EIGHT

ELLEN:

Most teenagers have experienced the desire to leave the family home and get out on their own. I was no exception. At the age of nineteen there were many reasons why I chose to look for somewhere to live by myself. I was pregnant, my Joe was in prison and home was just a collection of kids and a mother and father who spent most of their time having rows about everything under the sun.

I put the word about among my friends that I was looking for a place, which is how I came to meet Ginger O'Connor. He was one of the 'faces' in the Dale, quite a famous one in fact. He had been convicted of murder in 1942 and sentenced to death, but only a few days before he was due to be hanged he was reprieved. He had spent ten years in prison, and when he came out he took up writing for a living. He had a large house in Ashmore Road and let out rooms. Anyway I went round to see him and finished up taking the basement flat. It was just what I had been looking for.

I got to know Jimmy (Ginger was a nickname) fairly well. Nobody would have thought he was a murderer, he was a very gentle sort of bloke and, according to some people, a brilliant writer. He had married a woman called Nemone Lethbridge and they had a couple of kids. She was a barrister who had a lot of publicity when she defended Frank Mitchell, known as the Mad Axeman, when he was on trial for a stabbing offence.

Jimmy was well into the writing game and was also working hard on getting his case reviewed. He had only been out for about three years, but the way I saw it he had his work cut out if he was looking for a pardon. If I remember rightly one was handed out to Timothy Evans, but that was after he had been hanged, so it didn't do him much good. This Evans fellow was mixed up with Christie in what was known as the Rillington Place murders. Christie was also hanged, so the law got two for the price of one.

Jimmy always said that he knew the real murderer. He sent a fifty page application for a free pardon to the Home Office but that turned out to be a waste of time and paper.

I moved into the flat a little while before my baby was due. I didn't have to worry about money because my many friends and relatives were very helpful in that direction, also Joe was able to direct some cash my way even though he was in prison. At the time he was in Pentonville so I was in a position to visit him, the prison being on the other side of King's Cross and an easy bus ride from the Dale. He appeared to me to be resigned to spending the next few years in jail, but I heard through the grapevine that he had made an attempt to escape. This worried me quite a bit. If the escape had been successful he would have been on the run and life would have been very complicated.

I think I should explain about the grapevine, which is a way of smuggling news into and out of prisons and is quicker and more accurate than newspaper reports. It works in a number of ways despite the censorship of letters and other methods to prevent the outside world getting to know what goes on behind bars. The inmates themselves pass messages to each other, which is not all that difficult, and those messages find their way out through the system. An apparently harmless sentence in a letter can contain important information if the code is known. Add to that the constant procession of men being released, each one carrying messages to friends and relatives outside, and you get some idea of the difficulties the censors have to face, a game of cat and mouse with the mouse winning most of the time. I heard through the grapevine that Joe had been birched. I also knew that he had been transferred to Dartmoor about the same time as he got on the train at Paddington station.

I must admit my heart sank when I got that piece of news. I had heard stories about Dartmoor and I knew that Joe was not the sort of man who would take kindly to the life led by the inmates of that horrible place. I tried to console myself with what I knew about him, that he was tough and hard and would come through alright, but it didn't help much. I knew he was in for a rough time, but I couldn't do much other than hope and pray that he didn't run into serious trouble.

I now had to cope with my own problems. Shortly after my twentieth birthday I gave birth to our daughter in Queen Charlotte's hospital in Hammersmith. She was a bonny, healthy child. I called her Kim because I thought it was a name that suited her. I had a lot of support from all my friends and relatives. Aunt Kit was around most of the time and the Cannon brothers made sure that I did not want for anything. I won't say I was supremely happy, but I was much better off than many young mothers.

My first job when I got back to the flat with baby Kim was to make preparations for a trip to Dartmoor. As can well be imagined Joe was anxious to see baby Kim and I was equally eager to see Joe. I had to wait a while because it would have been foolish to take a new-born baby on a long train journey, but at last the day arrived when I got on the train at Paddington with my little Kim in my arms.

I have visited many prisons in my time, from Durham in the north to Parkhurst on the Isle of Wight, but of all of them Dartmoor was the most depressing. Getting there was anything but a pleasure trip but when I arrived my heart was in my boots. In fact, I very nearly turned back at the gates. It was only knowing that I was expected that gave me the strength to go inside. The first thing that hit me was the smell, a mixture of damp, decay and disinfectant. It was horrible.

The visit took place in a small room. Joe and I sat on either side of a wide table. There was a screw seated at each end, I don't know why because we were too far apart to touch each other. We exchanged a few words to which the screws listened intently, but it wasn't what could be called a happy occasion.

It was the first of many visits but I never got over my first impressions. Outside the gates I began to cry and wept all the way back to London as baby Kim slept on my lap. I had put on a front for Joe's sake and I'm sure he was also putting on an act for my benefit. So far as I was concerned I made up my mind that in the future there would be less weeping and more hoping. When I got back to the Dale I was ready for anything.

For the next few years there were no startling happenings. Joe's father died, which was a blow for the Cannon family. Joe wasn't at the graveside but there was a massive turn-out of family, relatives and friends. My dad got himself in a bit of trouble which led to me giving up the flat and moving back home to help out. Baby Kim fitted in well with the new arrangement and I was able to go out to work while mum minded her. One more kid didn't make all that difference to her. So the

130

days passed into weeks and the weeks passed into years and I grew older and wiser.

Came the day when Joe was released from Dartmoor into the land of the living. He didn't come chasing round to see me as soon as he got back to town, nor did I expect him to do so. A welcome home party had been organised for him, an all-male affair which took up a couple of days of his time. When he finally got round to sorting me out at my mum's he had fixed up a flat for us to move into right away, just round the corner from my Aunt Kit. How he managed it with a long queue on the council list for housing was a mystery, but he had a way of making things happen when he was determined to get something. We moved in, but hardly had we settled down than he was off on his travels. One of his favourite phrases was "see you later". Later could be that evening, a couple of days or a few weeks. I grew used to it.

One thing that my Joe never neglected was putting money indoors. He saw to it that Kim and I were well provided for. I didn't ask questions about where the money came from and he didn't volunteer any information. All I knew was that he had gone into the business of organising what were known as 'drinkers', illegal clubs which sold liquor at any hour of the day or night and were very profitable as long as they lasted. I didn't visit any of them but I knew what they were like from gossip, dingy premises frequented by peculiar people most of whom lived just on the other side from the law.

I suppose it could be said that I had nothing to grumble about at this stage in my life. I had a nice flat, there was no shortage of money and my five-year-old daughter was a joy. I took some pride in my home, everything was spotless and I was surrounded by friends. I could have done with seeing more of Joe but I accepted his increasingly long absences because I knew that he was intent on building up a chain of drinking clubs which, though illegal, were very profitable. I understood that he had to be there or thereabouts at all hours of the day and night and it would be wrong of me to complain since I enjoyed my share of the financial rewards.

About this time there was a lot going on in what the press referred as the underworld and the law was kept very busy. A gang had pulled off one of the greatest blags of all time when they robbed the Edinburgh to London mail train and got away with something like two and a half million pounds in used notes. In the manhunt that followed the Dale came in for its share of attention. Known criminals were roped in for questioning and for some considerable time it was impossible to walk round the manor without bumping into the law in some shape or form. Eventually the gang was rounded up, with a few notable exceptions, and sentenced to long terms of imprisonment.

The press had a field day over the Great Train Robbery. That was nothing to what was to come later, and the next lot was nearer home. It started with the discovery of the naked body of a prostitute on the riverbank at Chiswick. She had been strangled. The killing was reported in the papers and there was the usual guff about the police having several clues and an arrest being expected shortly. Well, there was no arrest but there was another murder, another brass found stripped and strangled. Now both these women had operated in the Notting Hill area and the law descended in force, running a fine tooth comb through the pubs and clubs and roping in suspects for questioning.

My feelings about brasses are, I suppose, shared by most women. Prostitution is well known as the oldest profession in the world and it's a safe bet that it's here to stay. Still, the thought of a woman selling her body for money and having sex with one man after another in the space of a few hours isn't very pleasant. Even more unpleasant is the danger of passing on sexual diseases, because it isn't every brass that insists on her client using a condom. However, my motto is live and let live, and if a woman wants to earn by selling her body then that's her business.

In that spring of 1964 tensions were running high in the Dale. The two murders had been linked together as the work of one killer and people began to gossip. On top of this a third murder took place about three weeks later almost exactly similar to the two previous ones. The press began to refer to these as the Nude Murders, and linked them up with three unsolved murders of brasses in the area between 1959 and 1964. This added up to a total of six killings which could all have been committed by the same person - or perhaps persons.

As I have said before, Joe did not talk to me about his doings and I didn't ask questions. Although he occasionally made the odd mention about his clubs it never occurred to me that he might be involved as a suspect in these killings. It came as a shock when the police questioned Joe's family and myself, making no secret of the fact that Joe was under suspicion. I had seen very little of him for quite a while but I put that down to the demands made on his time in running the clubs. The behaviour of the law threw a different light on his absence. He was obviously keeping out of the way.

The next thing to happen was that Joe was pulled in for questioning at the Yard. These things are supposed to be kept quiet but the word soon gets around and even though he was released without any charges against him he began to attract some queer looks. When mud is being thrown around some of it sticks. This didn't seem to bother Joe very much but it bothered me. I had a long talk with Aunt Kit which didn't help very much because she only repeated what she had said many times before, that Joe was my man and I should stick by him.

The problem I faced was simply this. Joe was a hard man, he went about with a gun stuck in his belt and I have no doubt that he was prepared to use it if the need arose. For all I knew he might have committed murder in the past and that thought tormented me. I remembered how he showed a lot of interest in the Christie business, turning up the reports on the case in the public library. What did it all add up to? Had Joe lost his marbles and set out on a crusade to clear the streets of brasses? Were his long absences really to do with his club ventures or was there a more sinister explanation? I read in the papers that the victims showed traces of paint on their bodies and the theory was that they had been killed at some other place than where the corpses were found. Joe's brother Nobby owned a row of lock-up garages where he stored all sorts of gear, including paint.

My mind was in a turmoil. I didn't know which way to turn. By now I was convinced that everything pointed to Joe as a mass killer and I dreaded the day when I would pick up a newspaper and read that he had been arrested. One thing I could not bring myself to do and that was confront him with my suspicions.

The days passed, the sensational stories faded out of the papers and the law seemed to have given up in the search for the killer. Joe popped in and out of the flat in his usual way as if he hadn't a care in the world, which only made my problem harder to solve. I did think at one point of clearing out with my little Kim, but what would happen afterwards? I finally made up my mind.

134

After all I wouldn't be the first woman to have lived with a killer and I was sure I wouldn't be the last, so I put the whole thing behind me and carried on with my life.

CHAPTER NINE

JOE:

It would be impossible to write anything about the underworld and its violence without mentioning the Kray twins, whose ex-exploits both in and out of prison have made headlines over the past quarter of a century. Books have been written about them, and they have figured largely in the memoirs of retired coppers. I have read everything I could lay my hands on, but nowhere in the vast mass of words have I been able to find what I would describe as the simple truth about these two characters. It can be expressed in three words. They were villains.

What is a villain? By definition he is a violent, malevolent or unscrupulous evil-doer who is low-born and base. What the dictionary does not say is that he lives in a separate world, apart from normal society, a world that lives by its own rules and very rigid codes. It is something the outsider can never hope to understand completely. On the inside, where I was, the understanding of these matters means the difference between survival and extinction.

Ronnie and Reggie Kray were, like myself and many others, natural-born villains, and villainy was our business. When we went out to capture our sometimes very considerable rewards, we made our own rules, which had nothing to do with Acts of Parliament. They could be expressed in a few words. The loot was shared out fairly and, if you were nicked, you didn't grass. Fail to obey the rules and you were either seriously injured or dead.

So where did the Krays and the Richardsons and the

Tibbs and the rest fit into society. The answer is, they didn't fit in at all. They killed and maimed each other for one reason or another, and the only members of the public who were involved were the idiots who tried to have a go and came out second best. I'll no doubt be accused of callousness, but there are certain facts of life of which everyone should be aware, and one of them is that the maintaining of law and order is best left to the Old Bill. By and large, when the amateur interferes in a row between professionals, he will inevitably get the shitty end of the stick. Let's put it this way. Who but a raving lunatic would jump into a ring where Cassius Clay (who prefers to be known as Muhammad Ali) and Joe Frazier were belting hell out of each other, and try to interfere with either man?

There's also another important point to be borne in mind. The Old Bill and the villain, both professionals in their different ways, have the measure of each other, and if a situation that looks like ending in bloody murder can be resolved by a touch of bribery and corruption then all's well that ends well. There's no trial, which saves the taxpayer's money, the over-crowded prisons don't become more overcrowded, the Old Bill cop a few bob and the villain skips off to Spain with the loot. The only lot to lose out are the insurance companies and they can well afford it. The whole set-up may be illegal and immoral, but it's practical.

As in any other section of society, vendettas and feuds happen in the underworld, but they last longer and are more violent than a quarrel between neighbours in suburbia. Some of the firms seemed to adopt a principle of 'if you're not with us, you're against us'. In the mid-sixties, when gang battles in the London area were giving the Met all kinds of headaches, I must have put a foot wrong somewhere.

The first indication of trouble came one evening when I was at a birthday celebration in the Jack of Clubs, a West End nightspot. I was with some friends of mine, Mike and Sue Donovan, who owned a pub in Seven Sisters Road called the Clarendon, and the occasion was in honour of Sue's birthday. Minding the club at that time was a fellow called George Cornell, who was later to get a bullet through the head in the Blind Beggar pub in Whitechapel Road. The man who fired the fatal shot was Ronnie Kray, but that's another story.

I had known George in prison and we got on quite well together. He came over to our table and chatted for a while, wished Sue a happy birthday and left. I had no suspicion that there was anything wrong, so I was surprised when one of the waiters came over and warned me in a whisper that Cornell was on the phone arranging for a firm to sort me out. I lost no time in gathering my party together and having it away. From the end of the street I watched two car-loads of heavies pull up outside the club. It was either the All-In-Wrestlers annual night out or Cornells reception committee, but I didn't wait to find out.

About a fortnight later a bloke named Bobby Cannon, an East End villain, but no relation, was grabbed by a team and stabbed before being driven away in the back of a van. The team had wrapped him up in a carpet, thinking he was dead, but in fact he was very much alive. When he came to he started chucking himself about and screaming and yelling, which was too much for the driver and his mate. They obviously didn't fancy explaining to the old Bill why their carpet was having a fit, which is probably why Bobby Cannon is still alive. They left the van with its load intact and scarpered.

It may have been that Bobby Cannon was mistaken for me or vice versa; or maybe it was another Cannon altogether who was down for a bit of treatment. It wouldn't be the first case of a mixup in a gangland feud which were becoming a feature of the criminal landscape in the sixties. Ginger Marks got himself shot outside the Carpenter Arms in Cheshire Street late one night, but it was all a mistake. Somebody else should have been on the receiving end.

It was a curious thing that the body was taken away and not left where it had fallen. The only other case I can recollect concerned Frank Mitchell, the so-called Mad Axeman, whose body also disappeared after a shooting. Maybe there was a connection between the two incidents. There was also Jack McVitie, again a disappearing body, but he was stabbed to death according to an eye-witness. Of these three killings only one was solved. Reggie Kray was convicted of his murder at the Old Bailey in 1968, although the defence claimed that Ronnie Hart wielded the knife that sent McVitie on his last journey.

These killings, and many others, were the outcome of underworld vendettas which are being carried on right up to the present time. Those concerned claim that it is nobody's business but theirs, and even the Old Bill seem to accept the situation with some reservations. I had the feeling that, somewhere high up in the private councils of the Met, a cynical group took the view that the more the villains bumped each other off, the less work they would have to do.

I may be over-simplifying, but it appears logical to me that the law should turn a blind eye to some of the goings-on until the time arrived when they had to do something. Then there would be a grand round-up, a spectacular trial at the Old Bailey with cars, vans and motor-cycles dashing around, screaming sirens and all the rest of the paraphernalia. All this may have terrified the public. It didn't frighten the villains one little bit. They let the dust die down and then carried on with the vendettas.

In 1970 David Knight, younger brother of Ronnie Knight, was stabbed to death in a London night club. Tony Zomparelli, adopted son of Albert Dimes, was found guilty of the killing and served four years for manslaughter.

In 1974 Zomparelli was shot dead in a Soho amusement arcade. Ronnie Knight, Nicky Gerard and George Bradshaw were brought to trial for the killing. Knight and Gerard were acquitted.

In 1978 Michael Gluckstead was shot and stabbed in the Norseman club in dockland. Nicky Gerard received seven years for grievous bodily harm.

In 1979 Johnny Mangan was shot at and left for dead in the East End. He survived. The man charged and acquitted of an attempted murder was Brian 'Little Legs' Clifford.

Peter Hennessey, landlord of the Dog and Gun pub in Deptford, was stabbed to death at a boxing gala in a Kensington Hotel. His killer was never found.

Mickey Hennessey, Peter's elder brother, was blasted by a shotgun through the side window of his car. His attackers escaped.

In 1980 Alfie Gerard, father of Nicky Gerard, was found dead in mysterious circumstances in a Brighton boarding house.

In 1981, during a fight in a club at the Elephant and Castle, Chris Byrne had his throat cut with a broken bottle and died from his injuries. The attacker, a man called Peter Kelly, was convicted of manslaughter and jailed for four years.

The body of Colin 'Dukey' Osborne was found on Hackney Marshes. He was on the run from the police, and evidence indicated that the corpse had been dumped from a moving car.

Club owner George Bell, a close friend of Peter Kelly, who had been jailed for the manslaughter of Chris Byrne, was shot twice in the stomach outside the City club near the Angel at Islington.

Towards the end of 1982 Nicky Gerard was shot to death outside his home. The two men who comitted the murder made their getaway.

Even as these words are being written, Patrick O'Nione, known as Paddy Onions, lies dead outside a wine bar in South London, victim of Assassins' bullets.

A fitting comment on this grim recital of murder and serious injury was provided by Barbara Windsor, actress ex-wife of Ronnie Knight.

'This has been going on for years,' she said. 'When is it going to stop?'

Came the spring of 1965 and I was in trouble again. I'd had a good run and pulled off several jobs, but the law caught up with me and I was in Brixton on remand on several charges of robbery which I reckoned would earn me five years. There was nothing to be done, so I settled back to enjoy the period of remand.

Being on remand isn't all that bad. A prisoner is allowed to wear his own clothes and have grub sent in from outside. Also, since he is technically innocent until proved guilty, he can't be put to work. This, as can be imagined, doesn't go down too well with the screws. So far as they are concerned, a con is a con, and shouldn't be permitted to strut about the boob smoking his head off and indulging in big eats. To even things up, they go out of their way to make things difficult for visitors bringing in the goodies.

When they tried this performance on with my Mum I

got the dead needle. She had come all the way from the Dale to pay me a visit only to be turned back by the screws at the gate. I heard about this through the prison grapevine, and went on Governor's application right away, determined to create a hell of a stink.

I've had quite a lot of experience of prison governors. Some of them are fair-minded men who are prepared to listen to what a con has to say but others are just arseholes, full of their own self-importance, having doors opened for them and being saluted wherever they go in the nick. The governor at Brixton was one of the arseholes. When I was escorted in to see him, a screw at my elbow, he didn't bother to look up from the papers on the desk in front of him.

'Yes, Cannon?' he says.

I tell him what happened to my mother and all he does is snigger, and the Chief Officer standing at his side has a quiet little grin. I look at this pair of cunts enjoying their joke at my Mum's expense and I'm almost beside myself with rage. What the hell can I do? I must do something. 'I don't see what you expect me to do about it, Cannon,' says the pompous shit.

This is the last straw. I've been dying for a piss while waiting outside the office and what follows is almost automatic. Quick as a flash I unzip my fly, take my prick out and, before the screw beside me can do anything to stop me, I have sprayed the governor with a cascade of hot, steaming piss. All hell is let loose. The screw jumps me and starts screaming for help, more screws rush in and I'm carted away, still pissing, to a padded cell in the hospital wing.

The news went round the nick like wildfire. Prison history had been made. There had been many previous instances of pisspots being emptied over screws or senior officers, but this was the first time in living memory that a governor had been deluged with the freshly made article. Even some of the screws had a good laugh over the incident. The governor was not all that popular with most of his staff either. I was kept in the hospital wing until the date of my trial, but I received no punishment for my breach of the 'thou shalt not piss over the governor' rule. I duly marched up the steps at the Bailey, copped for three years and was whipped off to Wandsworth, once again to be locked up in the hospital wing. There was now no doubt in my mind that the authorities suspected that I had gone round the bend, and were treating me like a fully-fledged lunatic. My inspired guess was confirmed when I was transferred to Tooting Bec hospital and placed under observation in a mental ward.

It's an ill wind that blows nobody any good, as the old proverb says. As I walked round the ward, muttering to myself like the rest of the loonies, I soon decided that having it away would be easy. Choosing the right moment, I smashed a window and was three-quarters of the way to freedom by the time the staff realised that one of their prize nutters was leaving them without permission. I felt hands closing round my ankles, but the ratio of Cannon outside to Cannon inside was about three to one, and the heaviest part won. I was wearing my own clothes, so I didn't stand out as an escaping jailbird, but I had to get off the streets as soon as possible. The Old Bill was liable to be out in force.

An old mate of mine lived in the Tooting area. I picked my way through the back streets, arrived at his house and knocked on the door, which was opened by my pal in person.

'Blimey, Joe,' he said. 'I thought you were away.'

'That's right. Away from Wandsworth.' I said. 'For fuck's sake let me in.'

With a new rig-out and a good few quid in my pocket, I was on my way the following morning.

I had my freedom, but I was on the run, which meant that I could not be seen about in my usual haunts. I tucked myself away south of the river, emerging from time to time for a spot of screwing, the proceeds of which built up my cash reserves. But I was just marking time. As usual, trouble was waiting for me round the next corner.

I suppose it was Ronnie Biggs going over the wall at Wandsworth that gave me the idea of making one on behalf of an old friend. Freddie Sampson was doing twelve, and it looked as though he would do the lot in Wandsworth, the most horrible prison in the British Isles. I could sympathise with him wanting to be out of it.

The escape party was five-handed. Adgie Pitts was at the wheel of the red Jag as we pulled up about thirty yards from the main gate of the jail just after one o'clock in the morning. There were two other blokes and a bird in support. I was the one to go in, with one of the other fellows helping with the gear, a knotted rope fitted with a grapnel, a rope ladder and a pair of bolt cutters.

The first hurdle was easy, the low wall of a house which led us directly to the main wall of the jail behind which was the hospital wing. I swung the rope, the grapnel clanged against the wall and fell back. I had another try with the same result. At the third attempt the grapnel lodged itself firmly on top of the wall and we were ready to go over. We waited for a few minutes in case the noise had aroused anyone either in the house or on the other side of the wall, but all was silent. We swarmed up the rope and sat astride the wall, looking out over the roof of a storeroom to the row of cell windows which formed part of the hospital wing.

Speed was now essential. We dropped down on to the roof and fixed the rope ladder to the guttering from where it hung down into the yard. Freddie was expecting us, and a glimmer of white showed where he had thrust his towel through the bars. Climbing down the rope ladder we were soon beneath the window. Freddie had already let down the drop-type frame behind the iron bars. Now all that remained to be done was to cut through those bars.

I had tested the bolt cutters, which sheared through inch square steel as though it was butter. What I hadn't taken into account was the fact that I would have to use them with my arms stretched up over my head. I couldn't get the leverage in that position, so we had to do a quick scout round to find something to stand on. Fortunately there was a pile of bricks close at hand from which we made a rickety platform. Bolt cutters at the ready, I jumped up and there was Freddie's pale, excited face only a few inches from mine.

The first bar was out in no time at all, and I was just starting on the second when the scream went up. Somebody inside the prison had pressed the alarm button. Freddy looked over his shoulder at the cell door behind him, which was slowly opening.

'Quick, Have it away. It's on top.' he gasped, and his face disappeared from my view as he dropped back from the window.

I dropped the cutters and ran. My mate was close behind me as we shinned up the rope ladder, pulled it up and shot across the storeroom roof. Lights were going on all over the place, the guard dogs were barking their heads off and there was enough row to waken the dead. We went down the rope ladder in double quick time and piled into the Jag, and Adgie was on the move before we had closed the doors. There was no need for words, it had obviously gone wrong and it was now up to Adgie to get us clear.

The man was pure magic with a car. In no time at all we were across the Common and into the back streets behind Tooting High Road. At the Broadway a couple of police cars had formed a road block. Adgie dropped down a gear, mounted the pavement and shot through, scattering Old Bill in all directions as he floored the accelerator. We were pursued for a while, Adgie doing things with the Jag which would have brought a set of 'tens' from the 'Come Dancing' panel and a cheer from the Jaguar design team. In the end we got clean away.

There was no mention in the papers of the attempt to liberate Freddy which, coming so soon after Biggsy's escape, was bound to raise questions about the Micky Mouse security measures at Wandsworth. I'm willing to bet that there were a few red faces at the Home Office, however, which was some reward for our efforts.

Adgie Pitts was killed in a car crash two years later, and Freddy Sampson was finally freed in tragic circumstances. He collapsed and died on the football field at Hull prison. Had our attempts to free him been successful he might have been alive and well today. Who knows?

After my brief career as escape organiser I lay low for a bit, but the need to earn some cash led me to team up with an Irish lad who was known as Tony Jenkins, though his real name was Doyle. He was one of the two uninvited guests who joined the Biggs-Flower escape in July. From what he told me, the getaway was a well organised doddle for which Paul Seabourne and Ronnie Leslie, the organisers, got top marks.

'We were out at exercise,' he told me. 'Biggsy and

Eric Flower was near the wall when these two ladders came over, and the two of them were halfway up before the screws realised what was happening. Some of the cons tackled the screws. It must have been all arranged. Anyway I thought I would have some of this, so I went over with another chap.'

'What did Biggsy have to say?' I asked.

'He was OK,' said Tony. 'Nice as pie. He dropped me and the other fellow at the station at Wandsworth Common. Wished us both good luck.'

That was very generous of Biggsy To see a pair of blokes take advantage of a scheme which must have cost him thousands could have ended in recriminations all round, but I suppose he took the view that his own escape had come off, so the rest was a bonus for anyone who got in on it.

Tony had a nice little earner lined up for us, a two-handed job which required that one of us would have to be disguised as a copper. What we have to do is to capture a uniform, so we case a house where an Old Bill lives and wait for him to go out. As soon as he leaves the premises with his little shopping bag we go in through the front door as bold as brass. We locate the uniform, make it into a tidy parcel and prepare to leave.

What we don't know is that we have been spotted entering the house and some nosy public-spirited character has rung the law. I open the front door to be fronted by a copper with an Alsatian dog on a lead backed up by what appears to be the entire duty roster from the local nick. I sling the uniform at the dog and a right-hander at its handler and then the fists begin to fly. While the dog is worrying the uniform, thinking there is a body inside it, the rest of the force descends on us and the battle commences. The outcome is inevitable. We are bundled into the paddy-wagon and carted off to the local nick where the duty sergeant is over-joyed to have a couple of notorious escapers brought back to the fold.

Now it's back to the old routine, appearance at the Magistrate's court charged with burglary and assault, a remand in custody to await trial at the Bailey and the long spell in Brixton while the prosecution assembled the case against us. Finally the day came when the might of British justice was ready to deal with the malefactors Doyle and Cannon.

I had a word with my Counsel in the cells underneath the Old Bailey before the trial started. He wasn't very comforting.

'It looks like a ten this time, Joey,' he said.

'Bloody lovely,' I replied, which was a sarcastic way of indicating that I didn't think it was lovely at all.

'Mind you,' he went on, 'we could try a plea under Section 60-65 of the Mental Health Act.'

I pricked my ears up at this one. 'what's it about?' I said.

'Well, it works something like this,' said my personal Rumpole. 'It says here that you pissed all over the governor at Brixton which indicates that there might be something wrong in the top story. Then you've got a record of persistent violence dating back to Borstal. Now if we make a plea under the Act, this would squash the three you were serving when you escaped, plus you would be sent to hospital for observation and reports.'

I gave this idea some thought, and it looked good.

'So how does it work out in practice?' I asked.

'You won't get a sentence,' said the brief. 'If the plea comes off, you'll probably go back to the hospital at Tooting Bec. They'll keep you there under observation, give you some treatment. As soon as they decide that you're OK, you'll be released. You should be out in six months or so.'

'Bloody lovely,' I said. I wasn't being sarcastic this time. Let's have a go.'

I was indeed very pleased. Instead of mailbags and pisspots, old barmy Cannon would be lying in bed eating grapes brought in by daily visitors and living the life of Riley. I almost skipped up two steps to the dock when the case was called. The charges were read out, both Tony and I pleaded not guilty as a matter of form, the judge nodded off and the trial proceeded.

To cut a long story short, Tony came out of it with just over six years after the consecutives and the concurrents had been sorted out. Then my turn came, and the old judge really let himself go. According to him I was a violent and dangerous character who rampaged around like Attila the Hun, leaving a trail of serious injury and destruction in my wake, and was suitable to be dealt with under the Act as a potential homicidal maniac. He made an order for detention and treatment under the relevant sections of the Mental Health Act and that was that. Good old Joey, I thought, as I danced down the steps, Tooting Bec here I come.

Alone in a cell in what had been the bowels of the old Newgate prison, I took stock of myself. Here I was, not yet thirty years of age, branded as a nutter by my own choice but knowing in my heart of hearts that I was anything but that. As I saw it I had taken the only way out of an impossible situation, impossible in the sense that I had been forced to choose between a long sentence of imprisonment and a temporary period in which I would be treated as a loony. Fine and dandy, I thought, I'll play the game according to the rules and make sure that I come out on top in the end. Or so I thought.

There was a rattling of keys and the cell door opened. A beefy copper I had not seen before stood outside.

'Right, Joey,' he said. 'Let's get going. Use the toilet now. We've got a long way to go.' A long way to go? Tooting Bec hospital was less than an hour from the Bailey. I did a quick piss and followed my escort out to the waiting van. I had no option but to follow him, because I was firmly attached by a set of Home Office Jewellery. When I saw that half-a-dozen Old Bill were sitting in the van I began to have misgivings, and I felt even worse as the vehicle headed north.

'Where are we off to then?' I said to the copper to whom I was handcuffed.

'Didn't you know?' he said we're off to Rampton.'

RAMPTON. Somebody had taken it seriously. What the hell had my brief done to me. I had heard stories about Rampton, and each one was worse than the last. What made it even more terrifying was that the rozzers in the van were humouring me, treating me as though I was a real nutter and a dangerous one at that. Not that there was much conversation; I had the feeling that the sooner they got rid of me the better pleased they'd be. The welcoming committee was a bunch of screws - I learned the hard way that they weren't screws but nurses, ha-bloody-ha and I don't think I've ever seen a more wicked-looking mob. They had evil grins on their faces and were obviously looking forward to introducing me to the delights of Rampton. It was my guess that they had been tipped off that I was a hard case, because as soon as they got me inside they went into a punching routine as I was hustled down a corridor.

'Think you're a hard man, Cannon' said one of them. 'We'll teach you. We tame lions here.'

I kept my mouth shut and didn't retaliate in any way as they wheeled me into a cell, known as a 'side room' for some reason. There they stripped me stark bollock naked, took my clothes and left me locked up for about an hour. Then two of them came in and proceeded to shave off every scrap of body hair, pubic hair and the lot. One of them took hold of my prick as he wielded the razor.

'You won't need this for a few years. Might as well whip it off, eh?'

His mate laughed. 'He could piss out of his fucking arsehole, couldn't he?'

They cracked a few more jokes at my expense. Every other word was four-letter Anglo Saxon. Then, still naked, I was led into a bathroom by one of them.

'Right, get yer dirty fucking body in there,' he said. The water was boiling. I looked for the cold tap, but there wasn't one.

'I can't get in there, guvnor,' I said. 'I'll be scalded.'

'Say 'sir' when you speak to me,' he said. 'Now, fucking get in there or I'll fucking put you in.'

No way was I going to step into that bath. The nurse stood there for a moment then went to the door of the bathroom and let out a yell into the corridor. In a twinkling the room was full of them, large, beefy blokes who had clearly been waiting for a signal. They were five-handed, and each one carried a knotted towel

'Right, cunt-face. Get in that fucking bath.'

'Bollocks.'

'OK, You've fucking asked for it.' They set to work on me after they had soaked the towels in water. By the time they had finished I was on the floor, feeling as though I had been through a concrete mixer. A knotted towel soaked in water doesn't sound like an offensive weapon, but believe me it can do some damage when there's a fourteen stone geezer at the delivery end.

That was my introduction to Rampton, but it was only a taster. I, who had never been frightened of anything or anybody in my life, began to know the meaning of fear. In an ordinary prison a con is able to take steps to protect himself not only against other cons but also against the odd screw who takes a dislike to him. In Rampton, where the screws - I can't bring myself to refer to them as nurses - all seemed to be related to each other, they ran the place. Not a day passed without some act of cruelty taking place. There was no discipline as such. The inmates were controlled by fear and the screws were responsible for the reign of terror.

My card was marked for me one day by a screw who didn't care for the look on my face when I passed him in a corridor. He gave me a pull right away. 'Come here, you fucking toe-rag,' he said.

I kept my distance. I had already been introduced to the screws sport of 'spine-dropping', kicking a patient's legs from under him so that he landed with a crash on his arse. 'Right you fucking monkey,' he said. 'I'll be watching you. We can fucking keep you here for ever. Don't fucking forget it.'

I had no intention of forgetting it, just as I had no intention of staying in that hell-hole for ever. I was in ward D2, a section reserved for violent and dangerous men, and I was treated as such. I was not allowed to shave myself. This was done for me on a hit and miss principle that left me looking like a mangy poodle. It was the same with the haircuts. It was all part of the overall scheme, to rob a man of the last vestige of his self-respect.

There were some sorry sights on the ward. There was Bernard, a bent and feeble figure confined to a wheelchair who, I was told, had been a fitness fanatic. Now he was a broken man with a pathetic waggling head and a pair of the biggest cauliflower ears I had ever seen. The stories about him were legion, how he had taken on whole gangs of screws and beat the shit out of some of them before he himself hit the deck. Whenever I looked at him I saw what I might become after a few years. The screws always gave him a wide berth. He had not lost his bottle and still wanted to have a go, even though his attempts ended up with him lying on the floor, when the screws would put the boot in.

Another pitiful case was a blind bloke called Jimmy. The screws tormented him something rotten, sneaking up behind him and clapping their hands over his ears so that he almost jumped out of his skin. Everything would go quiet as Jimmy called out, trying to identify whoever it was. 'Is that you?' he would call, and then wait for an answer. He knew the voices of all the men on the ward, but the screws would gesture to them to keep quiet so the poor blind sod would be wondering who was having a go at him.

A particular butt of the screws' perverted sense of humour was a big fellow they called Bonzo, who would sit for hours dragging on an unlighted cigarette and muttering obscenities against the screws under his breath. Two or three of the screws would come into the day room and pretend that Bonzo was a dog, making him get down on all fours and bark. The performance would go like this.

'Come here, Bonzo'' Bonzo would go down on hands and knees and crawl over to the screw.

'Ask for it Bonzo'

'Wuff, wuff, wuff.'

'Louder, you fucking tripehound, louder.'

'WUFF, WUFF, WUFF '

'Who's fucking shit on the floor then?'

'WUFF, WUFF, WUFF,'

Bonzo would then be on the receiving end of a good kicking and be ordered to go and lie down in a corner.

It was sickening to watch this degrading and humiliating business but nobody protested.

In an ordinary nick, if you had a complaint, you went on Governor's application and stated your grievance either to the Governor himself or his assistant. In Rampton the system was different. In the corner of the ward was a box with a slot in the top. If a patient had any complaint he was supposed to write it down and put it into this box, but he must first of all show it to the so-called staff nurse. Since most of the patients were illiterate, they were automatically ruled out. If the complaint was against a member of the staff it was torn up and thrown away. To sneak a written complaint into the box was impossible. It all added up to a sense of isolation from the real world which in itself was frightening.

Early evening was treatment time in ward D2, but don't run away with the idea that pills and medicines were dished out by the staff. The treatment was the screws' method of punishment for offences committed during the day, and was administered in an office at the end of a corridor leading from the ward. It was strictly unofficial, but then so were most of the goings-on in Rampton.

It would start with the name of the offender being called out by one of the screws in the day-room, where the patients sat around playing draughts or dominos or staring at a blank television screen. The miscreant would then walk along the corridor to the office where four or five screws would be waiting. The treatment would then commence with a volley of abuse followed by punchball practice and an occasional booting. If it went too far and the man was seriously injured, the screws would sort out one of the right idiots, accuse him of fighting with the injured geezer, lock both of them up and make out a report on the fictitious incident.

I witnessed one incident which even now, when I think of it, makes me shudder. One of the big fellows, a right loony but harmless, spoke out of turn to a couple of screws. They grabbed him and shoved his arm through a window repeatedly until it was almost slashed to ribbons and there was blood all over the place. The poor bloke was screaming in agony. One of the screws held him down while the other gave him an injection in the arse and put him spark out. They then made out a report that the man had tried to escape through the window. What I remember very vividly was the expressions on the faces of the two screws as they were performing. They were enjoying it.

I wouldn't want to give the impression that we were a timid lot being subjected to brutalising treatment by sadistic screws, because some of the patients were hard, tough and very dangerous. Curiously enough, they were the ones who kept out of trouble in the main. Those who copped for the most whackings were the big, simple-minded blokes. I tried to figure out what made the screws tick, why they seemed to enjoy brutalising fellow human beings, but I couldn't come up with a satisfactory answer. A partial explanation was, I suppose, that they had too much power and they tended to abuse it, added to which their job would be pretty boring if they didn't have a bit of excitement to look forward to.

There were a few decent blokes on the staff who tried to do a good job, but they were very much in the minority and were helpless in the face of the Nurses' Mafia. The hard core of brutes, long serving screws with family ties and roots in the locality, were in command, and God help anybody who went against them. If we are to believe the ex-Governor of the Scrubs, who referred to his prison as a penal dustbin, then by those standards Rampton was a bomb site, a derelict wasteland littered with bits and pieces of useless humanity, a property nobody wanted to develop.

At some time in the distant past some official had had the bright idea that the dreary lot of the inmates would be brightened by allowing the sexes to mingle at a weekly dance. At the time I was there the patients numbered about a thousand, six hundred men and four hundred women, segregated of course, and many of them looked forward to the dances as a high spot in the dreary routine. I went to a few of them. The scene beggared description. There they were, male and female loonies, jigging about to the music of a record player, the main object being to work their way to the middle of the crowd where, surrounded by jostling bodies, they would try to have it off. As soon as they were spotted the screws would dash in and separate them, and they were removed from the room. I don't know what happened to the woman, but the bloke was given the treatment, which was more painful and less satisfying than the quick fuck he had in mind.

As I saw it, the whole business was ludicrous. To pack three or four hundred sex-starved men and women into a room and permit them to have close bodily contact was looking for trouble. They had all been certified as mentally unstable and many of them were sex offenders. Whoever thought of the idea in the first place must have had a macabre sense of humour.

After a few months, during which I watched points and kept out of serious bother, I was beginning to get myself organised, I knew from the off that Rampton presented problems different to those encountered in the ordinary nick. To start with, I was surrounded by lunatics, which could be a bit of a nuisance. There were two blokes who were very retarded, children's minds in a grown-up body, who latched on to me and always tried to hold my hand when we were out at exercise. Another geezer looked on me as a father confessor and sorted me out to talk about his troubles. He was in for sexual offences against little girls and was an absolute nutter. He would corner me and describe in detail how he had used a razor to enlarge their vaginas, then go off muttering to himself about the shortage of small girls in Rampton. It was sickening, because the bloke really believed he had done nothing wrong.

There were a few fellows who were in the same boat as myself, completely sane but stuck away in Rampton for one reason or another. We tended to stick together, which was one way of preserving each other's sanity. I also had as many visits as the rules permitted, which had the effect of keeping the screws off my back to some extent. They weren't too keen on persecuting a patient who had regular outside contacts, the man without friends or relatives was an easier mark.

Toward the end of the first year I started having trouble with my back. The knotted towel-cum-spine dropping treatments had resulted in a bone being displaced. The pain was almost unbearable and there were times when I couldn't walk. At first the screws laughed at me, but in the end the doctor had to be called in. He was a young chap by the name of Nobel, and very bright. After he had given me a thorough examination in his surgery, we got to chatting.

"What are you doing here Cannon?' he said. 'You're not mental.'

I told him the whole story and he laughed.

'You've only yourself to blame,' he said. 'You should know better than to try to buck the system. However, I'm calling in an osteopath to see to your back. It looks

157

as though you will need to wear a corset for a while. By the way, how did you come by the injury?'

'I was lifting a bed,' I said. 'Then I got this sudden pain...'

I didn't have to say any more, The upshot was that I was fitted out with a steel-braced corset and transferred from D2 to the main hospital, where I was put on light duties. I was also recommended for release, came before a review tribunal and passed for discharge.

That wasn't the end of it. I was out of D2 and away from the real loonies, and all I had to do as a cleaner was walk round with a duster in my hand, but there wasn't a day passed that I wasn't shitting myself in case something went wrong. One morning I woke up and there was a black, furry thing on the pillow next to my head. I jumped out of bed, grabbed a shoe and was just about to beat it to death when I realised that it was a clump of my own hair which had simply fallen out of my scalp. Worry does strange things to a man.

It was to be a year before the Home Secretary put his signature to a piece of paper that said Joe Cannon wasn't mad any longer. three hundred and sixty five days each one of which seemed like a week. I came out of Rampton a wiser man, for it was there I learned the real meaning of words like fear and brutality and, above all, the depths of man's inhumanity to man.

CHAPTER TEN

ELLEN:

The other day I was thinking about some of my experiences, the people I had met and the situations I had been involved in. Taken by and large I feel I haven't much to complain about. There have been times when I've had to cope with some crisis or other when Joe has been away and I've had to rely on family and friends for support, but I've never been let down. As a well-known face in the brotherhood of villains Joe was respected and some of that respect rubbed off on me. We didn't live in any great style but our home was always spick and span and visitors were made welcome. As can well be imagined some of the visitors were anything but upright and honest citizens, but birds of a feather flock together as the saying goes. Sometimes I'd walk into the sitting room and there'd be three or four fellows sitting there, talking in low voices as if they were afraid of being overheard. I recognised most of them but apart from the usual greetings we didn't exchange words. I knew my place and, on those occasions, kept out of the way.

I remember one time vividly. A couple of well-dressed blokes came in with Joe and he took them into the sitting room. I went in later to see if they wanted a cupper and found that the curtains were drawn and the music on the radio going full blast. The blokes had American accents and they insisted on these sort of antics because they were dead scared of being bugged and having their conversations recorded. I met many of them from time to time, members of the international crime ring known as the Mafia.

Mention the Mafia and most people think about the gangs which flourished in the United States during the prohibition era. They also think that the Mafia is only existing on the other side of the Atlantic. I have news for them. The Mafia has been operating in Britain for years. The skim money from the casinos of Las Vegas has financed many straight business ventures here and on the Continent. It's what is known as 'laundering', converting bent dollars into European currencies, and it's been going on for decades. God knows how much the US taxman has lost, but it must run into millions.

There was a massive invasion of these Mafia characters when gambling was legalised in the early 60's when casinos sprang up like mushrooms all over the country. Joe took me out one night to a West End gambling club, where we met George Raft. He had left off playing gangsters in films to play host at the club, but he didn't last long. He was deported as an undesirable alien but he left many of his colleagues behind. Some of them are here to this day, dealing in a much more dangerous activity than separating a mug from his money via the roulette wheel and the blackjack table. The trade is drugs and the rewards enormous. To my knowledge a lot of villains won't have anything to do with the drug traffic, but there are some who are tempted by the huge profits to be made.

There is no great risk to the organisers behind the transport of cannabis, heroin and cocaine from Colombia and Pakistan to the United States and Europe. The work is done by the carriers (known as moles) and they suffer the punishment when a cargo is intercepted by Customs. The moles get up to all kinds of tricks, which

160

1. Mum; Ellen; Dad

2. Ellen and baby Kim

3. Ellen and Joe

4. Ellen and baby Kim in the hop-fields

5. We are the Notting Dale Girls. Ellen in middle of group

6. Al Pacino. Jimmy Cannon

7. Donald Sutherland. Jimmy Cannon

8. Joey, centre, with some of the local hounds. Second from left,
Terry Buckingham, who was stabbed to death
in Wakefield Prison, 1964

9. Joe and Jimmy Cannon

10. Nobby Cannon. Third from left. Local pub.

11. Left to right outside The Vic, Latimer Road, W11. Johnnie Mole; Tommy Cannon; Alfie Bridges; Winterflood and Frenchie.

12. A unique photograph. Left to right, Emma Kirk;
Artie Cain; Nobby Cannon; Nat Johnson; Lassie Burton;
Aaron Kirk;

13. Ex-Mayor of Hammersmith and Fulham, Fred Innis,
a Notting Dale boy that made good

14. Day outing for the mums with The Dolphin local pub

15. The Brit in Clarendon Road, Notting Dale, ladies outing

16. The local, Bridport Arms,
corner of Avondale Park Road, Notting Dale.

17. Ellen, fifth from left, on day trip to Southend, 1971
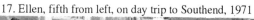

18. A group of the Notting Dalers.

19. A few of the lads.

20. Local 'lads' from Portobello Market

21. Rampton, 1966. Joey with some of the
most violent men in Britain

22. Joe, third from left, with some well known faces.

23. In 1979, Johnny Mangan was shot and left for dead in the East End. He survived. Joe Cannon. Mangan was Joe's driver.

Joe Cannon   Beryl Gibbons   Cynthia Payne
Licencess of the   (Madam Sin)
famous Thomas
A'Becket Pub
& Gym

25. Ellen and Joe Longthorne

26. Caroline Graham. Joe Longthorne. Joe Cannon

27. Second from left, Tony Doyle, who went over the wall at Wandsworth with Ronnie Biggs. Joey is second from right.

28. Left to right, Charlie Kray, Joey, and friend Basil.

29. Joey among the Pearly Kings and Queens.

30. Left to right: Jim Scott (Producer); Martin Short (Author);
Joe Cannon.; Micky Moynihan; and family friend

31. John H. Stracey. British Welterweight Champion and Joe
Cannon. A night out.

32. Joe, Nobby, Ellen, Josie.

33. Joe and Ellen.

meet with considerable success because Customs officers admit that ninety per cent of smuggled drugs get through their controls. The drug traffic is a multi-billion dollar business financed and run in the main by that one organisation with the funds and the international criminal connections to manage it - the Mafia.

How do I know so much about these goings-on? The answer is simple. When you are involved with criminals and keep your eyes and ears open you can't fail to know. A few words are dropped here, a bit of gossip is picked up there, add two and two together and you get the picture. What's more, you don't have to be super-intelligent to suss it out.

Getting back to the Dale and that summer of 65, Joe was once more in trouble. So far as I could gather his club ventures had gone down the pan and he'd gone back to thieving. He must have done quite well because he was not short of money. Still, blagging is a risky business and one day his luck ran out, so it was a nicking and remand in custody in Brixton prison to await trial at the Old Bailey. I did the usual, arranging for food and other comforts to be sent in, visiting as often as possible and so on. A prisoner on remand has a lot of privileges such as being allowed to wear his own clothes and things like that. It's the law, a man is innocent until he's proved guilty. Joe took full advantage of that. He must have presented the screws with some problems.

It was in Brixton that the real bother started. The story, as I heard it, was that Joe's mother was refused permission to see him and was turned back at the gates. Joe got the hump, went before the governor to complain and was laughed at. The story goes that he pissed all over and injured a few screws in the process. The governor collected a share of the piss, Joe was carted off to the hospital wing under restraint and was later transferred to a hospital in Tooting for observation. It was clear that the authorities thought that he had gone round the bend.

To cut a long story short, Joe had it away from the hospital, did a few jobs during his period of freedom but was picked up and finally went up the steps at the Bailey for trial. He faced a string of charges as long as his arm. In the result Joe was sent to Rampton, a high-security prison, for an indefinite period. The word went round the Dale that Joe Cannon was now branded as a nutter, but I was quite sure that he had tried to pull a stroke which hadn't come off.

As everybody knew, Rampton was a prison for loonies. My great fear was that Joe would be affected by being shut up with mentally disturbed criminals but I am glad to say that those fears turned out to be unfounded. It was a couple of years before he regained his freedom, but he came out of Rampton pretty much the same as when he went in. I must say this for him, he was a tryer. He turned his back on the Dale, where he was too well-known to be comfortable, opened up a minicab business in Kentish Town and started earning again.

My memories of this stage in my life are confused. There was a lot going on, villains being nicked right left and centre. The Richardson brothers from South London were on trial at the Old Bailey and the London underworld was buzzing with rumours that the Kray twins, Ronnie and Reggie, were the next in line for the same treatment. Joe had connections in both camps, so he was on a tightrope. As I remember he was mixed up with some local villains in a protection racket in West London. There were two brothers, Alan and Billy Mills, and another chap , Charlie Canavan.

I had met the Richardson brothers and also the Kray twins and their brother Charlie on several occasions. The elder Richardson, Charlie, seemed to me to be a very nice fellow as was his young brother Eddie, and I could hardly believe the stories that were told at their trial about torture sessions when they were accused of committing horrible atrocities on some of their associates. As for the Kray twins, well, there's such a lot that has been written and said about them that they have become household names. Their mother Violet was one of the most wonderful women I have ever met. Her little council Flat in the East End was always shining neat and tidy. She thought the world of the twins and wouldn't hear a wrong word said against them.

Joe was already into a sentence of four years when the twins went to trial. He was serving his time in a new prison at Blundeston which he told me was a piece of cake. It was a specially built jail block, so there was no slopping out. Also the discipline was much less strict than in the usual run of prisons. I must say that my visits there impressed me.

There was a lot of tension in the Dale about this time. Practically every villain on the manor had been connected with the Kray twins at some time or other and there was a feeling among them that they might be pulled in and asked questions which would lead to unsatisfactory answers. As a result many of the well-known faces did a disappearing act. It was common gossip that Chief Superintendent Leonard 'Nipper' Read, who was in charge of the case against the twins, was going all out to get them put away for a very long time and wasn't all that particular about the methods he used.

The twins and some of their mob came up for trial at the Old Bailey on the 7th of January 1969. The papers were full of it, headlines in heavy print and pages of reports about the proceedings. I don't think that anybody read these reports more closely than I did. I lived in constant fear that Joe would be involved somewhere along the line but, although he was brought from Blundeston to give evidence for the Kray's, I was relieved about that. I know he would not have said a word against the twins, it wasn't in his nature.

What was my personal opinion of the twins? I can only speak as I find. Being villains they behaved like villains and they couldn't do other than that. Ronnie, who was nicknamed the Colonel, was a ruthless man who wouldn't stand for any nonsense from either friend or enemy. He was also capable of great generosity which was sometimes misdirected. He had a great respect for old people and always treated the womenfolk in his circle with politeness. Bad language in their presence was out of the question and anybody who was guilty of breaking that rule was in serious trouble. Perhaps the worst thing about him was his terrible temper. Nothing could be done with him if he was in one of his rages.

His twin brother, Reggie, was just as tough but was a quieter character altogether. I thought he was more dangerous in a way than Ronnie. He would go into a situation without giving any indication of what he was going to do about it, then suddenly he would spring into action with disastrous results for the other party.
I must mention the elder brother Charlie, who was as different as chalk from cheese to the twins. He was a very easy-going fellow with a lot of charm and a way of fixing things when they looked like getting out of hand. He was, as far as I could see, never involved in the twins' excesses although he was always on hand to come to the rescue when there was any serious trouble.

When the twins were sent down for thirty years Charlie got ten years for, it was said, helping to dispose of the body of Jack McVitie. It was common knowledge that he had nothing to do with that business. However, as far as the law was concerned he was a Kray so down he went.

The convictions of the Richardsons and the Krays and their respective gangs was regarded as a great victory for law and order, but I have my doubts about that. They are written and talked about right up to this present day and in some quarters they are regarded as folk heroes. The papers made headlines about the end of gangsterism in Britain yet as everyone knows crime still flourishes. The old-time mobsters have been replaced by more sophisticated villains who have learned much from the past. Organised crime has become an international affair and is a highly sophisticated business. As criminals are brought before the courts and sent to prison for long stretches there are others waiting to take their places. Villains are not only to be found in the breeding areas of the East End. They now exist in the boardrooms and speak in the educated accents of public schools and universities.

CHAPTER ELEVEN

JOE:

Coming out of Rampton was like being released from a nightmare into a world peopled by real human beings, although a reminder of that hell-hole was by my side all the way to Notting Dale. The regulations said that I must be accompanied to my home by a screw, but I was so relieved at getting out that I wouldn't have minded being taken home by old Lucifer himself.

When we arrived at King's Cross I fell out with my travelling companion. He wanted to go on by tube, but I wasn't having any of that. I was now on my own manor, back in the smoke, and it was a taxi for me. I debated giving him the slip, but decided it wasn't worth it. The result was we turned up at the Dale in a cab and I felt like a member of society again as I paid the cabbie and invited the screw indoors for a cup of tea.

Mum was, as always, glad to see me, but the screw put his foot in it again. He started rabbiting about how much money I had on me and suchlike, as though I was a naughty kid who couldn't be trusted. I soon put a stop to that.

'Look, mate,' I said. 'You can leave that out. Sit down, have a nice cupper, and then I'll buy you a nice drink before you go back .'

He got the message. Just then my brothers Billy and Nobby walked in the door. I marked their cards about the screw, who was invited to come and have a drink with us. I intended to get him well pissed and send him back to Rampton in a right old state, but it didn't work.

He had a light ale at the local and went back to Rampton, and I wasn't sorry to see the back of him. With his departure I was finished with Rampton.

For a few weeks things were a bit strange. I stayed on the manor because I felt secure among people I knew, but even some of them gave me funny looks now and then, as though they expected me to suddenly foam at the mouth or swing from a chandelier or something like that. Yet what disturbed me most was Mum's reaction to me. She had always been a jewel, visiting me when I was away, looking after me when I came home cut to pieces and never questioning the way I lived. Now she had a long talk with me, and made it plain that she was getting too old to put up with this sort of lark, so if I got into trouble again the door was closed.

During the two years I had been away there were big changes. The Old Bill had been very active. The Richardsons had been nicked, and in June of 1967 were put away for a very long time. Charlie, who is now out, got twenty-five years. Then in May of 1968 three months before I was let out of Rampton, the Kray firm was also nicked and were banged up in Brixton awaiting trial. Naturally, everybody who had had any sort of connection with the Krays was a bit jumpy, including myself, because we ran the risk of being pulled in for questioning.

About that time there was an outbreak of demanding with menaces in the pubs in the Notting Hill area. Quite a few of them were smashed up and several people got cut, so the publicans got together and brought in the Old Bill to clean things up. I'm in the Derby one night with a few mates when somebody comes up on me from behind and sticks a shooter into my back. The band is belting away and there's a lot of noise going on. This bloke whispers right in my ear. 'You're nicked, Joe,' he says.

I started to walk out of the pub with this geezer treading on my heels. The band stopped playing, and I noticed that Alan and Billy Mills were being hustled out of another door. Out on the street I was shoved into a car, an ordinary saloon with no markings. As I sat there the Mills boys started yelling something about a trap and there was a pitched battle on the pavement. A police van came swinging round the corner and a dozen Old Bill jumped out. It was a real round-up. I heard later that half the villains in Notting Dale got their collars felt.

As far as I was concerned, along with Alan and Billy Mills and a chap called Charlie Canavan I was done for robbery and damage to a pub and remanded in Brixton. The Kray mob was also there, but they were kept in a special cage well away from the other prisoners. I had a feeling that there was something funny going on, and when I heard through the grapevine that Nipper Read, who had personally nicked Ronnie and Reggie Kray, was spending a lot of his time interviewing villains in a private room at Brixton I got the wind up. The last thing I needed was to be involved in the Kray trial. As things turned out, I couldn't avoid

Chief Superintendent Leonard Read, to give the Nipper his official title, was in charge of the operation of building up a cast-iron case against the Kray twins. As soon as they were safely banged up in Brixton, he could put himself about to gather a mass of evidence against them, most of which came from villains who were already inside, either serving sentences or awaiting trial. It was all very simple. They grassed the twins, the law granted them certain favours and everybody was happy. All, that is, except Ronnie and Reggie. That was where I came into the picture. When the Mills brothers, Charlie Canavan and myself went on trial at the Old Bailey in October, I had cocked up a story with Alan Mills to mention that I had met him in prison. It was an old dodge, but such a mention would lead to a retrial at which there was a chance of either getting chucked or coming out with a lighter sentence. Now, what does this louse do but change his plea to guilty halfway through the trial and throw himself on the mercy of the court while dropping the rest of us, including his brother Billy, right in the shit. He has done a deal with Nipper Read to give evidence against the Krays. As a result, although he has more charges against him than the rest of us put together, he gets off with two and a half years. Billy gets eighteen months, Charlie Canavan nine months and I cop for four years.

I was sent to Blundeston to serve my sentence, about which I shall have something to say later. What was more important, the Kray trial opened at the Old Bailey on the 7th January 1969 and was to go on for two months. The twins were up on charges of murder. Ronnie was accused of shooting George Cornell in the Blind Beggar pub, Reggie of stabbing Jack 'The Hat' McVitie to death in a house in Evering Road, Stoke Newington.

The deal Alan Mills had done with Nipper Read was as follows. Mills was to testify that he had been with the Lambrianou brothers when McVitie was lured to the house in Evering Road where he was stabbed to death. I don't know whether Mills was present or not, but I do know that, since both Chris and Tony Lambrianou were on trial, they could hardly be expected to convict themselves. So, without the evidence of Alan Mills, it would have been difficult to establish that McVitie actually went to the 'birds and booze' party. I was brought from Blundeston to give evidence for the defence, but I might as well have been saved the journey and my breath.

I'd like to say, here and now, that I have never been

a grass, I have no intention of being a grass and, in my view, grasses are the lowest form of shitcunt in the criminal world. Without the assistance of grasses, Nipper Read wouldn't have had a chance in hell of getting the Krays convicted. Mind you, I'm not trying to whitewash the twins. I've known them since I was sixteen. They were villains, just as I was, and violence was a part of our lives. Sooner or later we all got hurt, one way or another.

A final word about Alan Mills. When we were up at the Old Bailey together, prosecuting counsel opened the proceedings with a thumbnail sketch of this bloke's character. 'Wherever Alan Mills goes,' he said, 'violence follows him. He is a man who thrives on violence.' Giving evidence at the Kray trial, Mills said he saw the murder being done and was *terrified* (my italics). This from a geezer who'd cut your head off as soon as look at you. Beats cockfighting, don't it?

Back to Blundeston, and I felt as though I had been sent to a convalescent home. As compared to the other prisons in which I had served sentences it was a dream. The majority of the inmates were habitual criminals but most of the staff, from the governor downwards, treated them like human beings. There was none of the shouting and bawling, 'Get in line', 'Lead on', 'Stop talking' and that sort of thing. Also the buildings were new and specially designed. There was always free access to toilets at any time, so the degrading 'slopping out' routine wasn't necessary. Incidents of violence were very rare indeed, and it was the smoothest-running prison I have ever been in. It was also the only prison where I was never on report and didn't lose a single day remission. Thus my four years became two years and eight months.

One story is worth telling. A mate of mine, Chris

Wilkins, wanted to get married while he was serving his sentence, and applied to the governor for permission. It was granted, and Chris was let out, under guard of course, for the ceremony. A few of us, decided that the occasion should be celebrated, so we threw a party for him. It's almost unbelievable, but with the help of a friendly screw we got together the necessaries, including a supply of booze, and had a high old time. I was to see a lot of Chris in the ensuing years. We often had a good laugh about what must have been the most unusual wedding breakfast of all time.

I had my reward for being a good boy. The last six months of my sentence was spent in the hostel and I was allowed to go out to work from Monday to Friday. I was found a job at a local factory, a sort of knacker's yard where dead animals were processed for all kinds of purposes. It wasn't the kind of job I would have picked for myself, but it made a change. I worked on the ramp, where the carcases were loaded on to a conveyor belt from the delivery lorries and, though it wasn't the most pleasant of tasks to handle three-day-old dead meat, there were compensations. The carcases contained masses of fine, healthy maggots, and we did a roaring trade with the local fishing enthusiasts. We didn't want for pocket money.

I had a few visits from Vi and Charlie Kray, the twins' parents who, in spite of their own troubles, still found time to make the journey from London to see me. I knew, of course, that the twins had each got life with a recommendation that they should serve thirty years, and Charlie had got ten for allegedly having helped to dispose of Jack McVitie's body along with Freddie Foreman. I really felt sorry for Vi, but I must say that she didn't wallow in self-pity but went all out to try and help her sons in whatever way she could. There were a lot of people who missed her when she died in '82. She was a very remarkable woman.

The day came when I was released, but I didn't go home. My Mum had stuck to her word and put the bar up, for which I really couldn't blame her. I went to work on the Kentish Town manor, where I teamed up with a Greek bloke running a minicab business and also opened a fruit stall in Leyton Road, just outside a pub called the Gloucester Arms. I was going straight.

It was reported in the press, just another robbery in the catalogue of London crime. The time was ten thirty on the evening of Monday, 7th February 1972. In the Duke of Edinburgh, a pub on the corner of Queensway and Moscow Road in Bayswater, Mrs. Nora Clarke was drinking with her friend, a young man by the name of Dennis Price.

Mrs. Clarke was a regular customer at the pub, where she was known as a good punter. She threw her money about at the same time as she flashed a load of high-class tom, which was an invitation for any villain looking for an easy mark. The three men sitting in the Austin Cambridge saloon parked in Moscow Road had accepted the invitation. The lady was due for a shock

Shortly after eleven o'clock Mr. Price and the lady emerged from the Moscow Road entrance - or should it be exit - of the pub. Mrs. Clarke's two small dogs cocked their legs against the nearest lamp post while the lady leaned affectionately against her escort. A few yards away, two men sprang from the back of the Austin and stood waiting as the couple approached them.

There was suddenly the sharp odour of lemon juice in the air as the men discharged the contents of the plastic containers they were carrying into the faces of their victims. As the lady screamed and her escort staggered blindly on the pavement, one of the men put a full nelson on her and fell backwards with her into the rear of the car. While the other man leaped in beside the driver. The car was off into Queensway, scattering the pedestrians to right and left.

In Inverness Terrace, scarcely a mile from Moscow Road, the car came to a halt. By that time the unfortunate lady had been stripped of her rings, bracelets, brooches and watch, everything save the keys of her flat had been taken from her handbag and she was left dazed and helpless as her attackers climbed into another car and sped away.

The lady was not hurt. The Old Bill took her to the nearest hospital where she was treated for shock, given a cup of tea and sent home.

Some months later I was to be charged with taking part in the robbery.

To return to the Kentish Town scene, I put in a lot of work at the mini-cab business, which became a money-spinner. Greek Andy, my partner, ran the garage in the downstairs part of the premises. I had an office on the first floor over the garage where, with the help of a controller, I ran the fleet which grew bigger every day. Only an idiot could fail to make money at this game. The drivers owned their own vehicles, and all I had to do was to take them on, fit them out with a radio and collect a weekly payment from them. They land all expenses, including petrol and Hire and Reward insurance, and were responsible for repairs. Greek Andy carried these out in the garage, so we had two bites at the same cherry.

Advertising was no sweat. I plastered the whole of Kentish Town with cards, and the business rolled in. We didn't bother much with account customers. Cash was what we were after and it was cash we got, so I always had a wallet stuffed with readies and bollocks to the commissioners of Inland Revenue. The game was so good that a lot of villains with a bit of cash to spare jumped on this profitable bandwagon and, as the competition hotted up, took to using shooters to enforce their territorial rights. This was in the future, as I shall describe later. At that time my only worry was Greek Andy, who was turning out to be a very dodgy character indeed.

I turned up at the office one morning and found a stranger sitting at my desk and going through the books which, although rough and ready, gave a good idea of the state of business. Naturally I asked him who he was and what he was doing.

'I'm Andy's brother-in-law,' he said. 'I just wanted to see how you were getting on.'

'That's none of your fucking business,' I said. 'Come on. Out.'

He got up meekly enough, and I carted him off downstairs to sort things out with Andy. The two of them started jabbering away in Greek. I soon put a stop to that.

'I don't know what you pair of shitcunts are up to,' I said, 'but don't mess about with me.'

A worried look appeared on Andy's face. He knew what I was capable of doing to anybody who tried to work a flanker on me.

'Nothing to worry, Joe, nothing,' he said. 'My brother-in-law own lease. He renew it for us.'

I had to leave it at that but I was fairly sure that Andy wouldn't do anything silly. I couldn't have been more wrong. The lousy little bastard set me up, which I discovered when I arrived one morning to find the place swarming with Old Bill. The premises had been broken into and cleaned out, and it was obvious to me that it was Andy's work. With my form I had no chance. I was nicked. A grinning Andy watched me being taken away.

Back once more in Brixton on remand, I am seething. That little Greek bastard has worked a right flanker on me, and here I am, nicked for nothing.

Since the last time I've been in residence there, Brixton has become even worse. The conditions are terrible, the screws are leaning on everybody and my card is marked because of the episode when I pissed all over the Governor. I meet up with a few old pals, among them Chris Wilkins who was with me in Blundeston. All the remand men are really pissed off, and one fine sunny day we do something about it. At the end of the morning exercise period we sit down in the yard and refuse to go back inside.

There isn't much the screws can do about the situation. We don't indulge in any violence, we just sit there on our arses and don't budge. The deputy Governor comes down and does a bit of shouting and hollering, but for all the difference it makes it is a waste of his breath and our time. Lunch time comes and goes and we are still sitting there, but it's not very comfortable since it's a very hot day and there's no shade in the open yard. We are all dying for a cupper and something to eat. I'm sitting with Chris and a couple of other blokes, Ray 'Scarface' Pegler and Richie Payne, who is called 'Honeypuff' because he's such a clumsy sod, and as I look around at the hundred or so fellows who all have the same idea about protesting, I realise that a bit of geeing-up is all that's required to start a mass breakout.

Our little group starts chanting, stuff like 'why are we waiting' and so on, and some of the others take it up, but it comes to nothing. Most of the geezers rumble what we're up to and don't want to be involved in anything serious, so they get up and go back inside. By the evening it's all over, but I'm still thinking about the possibilities of stirring up a mass escape.

In any remand prison escape fantasies flourish. Irish gas meter bandits put it about that they can organise their mates in the IRA to blow a hole in the wall. Then there's the bloke with a friend who is a helicopter pilot who gives you a load of verbal about Fearless Fred hovering over the exercise yard as swarms of cons climb rope ladders to freedom. Others claim to have a team on the outside who will storm the wall, come over the top brandishing knifes, choppers and shooters, and open the gates. After listening to some of these merchants, I think I am back in Rampton.

I give some thought to the business, and it doesn't seem be to me to be all that difficult, so I collect a little team and ask them what they think. There's Chris Wilkins, Ray Pegler and Ritchie Payne, who are all for it, and we rope in big Harry Turner and Leroy Davies Davies, by the way, later turned informer and put a lot of men away. Then a good man by the name of Obie O'Brien gets interested and says he will make one. I am building up a little mob who can be trusted to perform when the moment arrives.

There is a small fly in the ointment. A geezer called George de Buriatte has got a whisper, and he comes to me asking to be let in. Somehow I don't trust the fellow, so I laugh it off and tell him he's been dreaming, but I still feel uneasy, so I tip my partners off to keep clear of this merchant.

The first step in the plan is for a couple of us to be unlocked in the evening, so Ray and myself get on to a works party which is doing a bit of painting on the wing. We wangle this through an old mate Jimmy Moore, who is well in with the screws as he does some of their bookwork for them. We are unlocked at six every evening, issued with paint and brushes, and then left more or less on our tod to get on with the job. After a few days we have the routine pretty well taped and fix on a Sunday night as being the best bet. We have discovered that there's only a skeleton staff on duty.

We pass the word during exercise on Sunday afternoon just before we are locked up. Ray and I are in adjacent cells on the ground floor of A wing, the others are on the fours. I have a mug of tea beside me but I can't drink. During the next two hours the tension mounts. Will the screw unlock me and Ray on time? Has the plot been sussed? The excitement has a reaction and I keep wanting to piss. I am wearing my suit under my overalls, so I'm sweating like a pig. I finger the 50p piece in my pocket, and wonder if I'll get to spend it on the outside. Then suddenly it's six o'clock and I hear the welcome sound of a key being turned in the lock of my peter.

The screw pokes his head in. 'Painting tonight, Cannon?' he says. I tell him I won't be a minute, and step out just as Ray is being unlocked. Stuffed inside my overalls is a real double-lively hard porn magazine which is going to be bait for the older of the two screws, who is a right dirty old fucker. I wink at Ray and we start getting our gear together. Then, right on the dot at five minutes past six, a bell rings on the fours. Chris Wilkins' finger is on the button. It's all part of the plan.

It works out as we thought it would. The old screw looks at the indicator. 'Oh, shit,' he says. 'Up on the fucking fours. Nip up and see to it, Fred. Your legs are younger than mine.'

It's all going for us. As soon as Fred starts his climb to the fours I pull the mag out from inside my overalls. 'Here, guv,' I say. 'Got a new mag here. A right beauty.' I hold it up so that he can see the cover, which is very lurid indeed. I bank on him walking over to take it from me so that I can bundle him into my peter, lay him out and tie him up. It doesn't come off.

'Let's have it, Cannon,' he says, holding out his hand.

I had no option but to go over to him and hand him the magazine. He takes it without a word and moves over to the recess where the light is better. As he turns the pages his eyes are almost popping out of his head. I look over at Ray, who nods his head, and I go into action.

I have reached the screw in a few quick strides. He has no chance. I claim him and clamp my hand over his mouth, kick his feet from under him and we hit the deck together. His hat has fallen off in the struggle. As Ray rushes up with some bits of rope the silly old sod tries to bite my hand. I grab him by the hair to pull his head back and find myself holding a handful of wig. Then, all at once, my other hand is full of false teeth. Christ, I thought, the poor bugger's coming apart in my hands.

Nothing else falls off him as we tie him up and stick a gag in his mouth. We carry him into the recess, I get his keys and we are ready for the next stage, which is to claim the screw who by now should have reached the fours. It was then that it starts to go wrong. I should explain that, when a con rings the bell in his cell, a metal indicator drops outside the door. The screw, on his way to the fours, has noticed that there is an indicator down on the threes, and has gone to see to it. Consequently, as we reach the threes landing, there's the screw, a few yards away and giving us a hard look. Next minute he's off down the landing like a greyhound. If he reaches the alarm bell, that's the end of the escape. He doesn't. Ray and I collar him with yards to spare.

He isn't a lot of trouble. In fact, as we drag him into

178

the landing recess and proceed to gag him and tie him up, he shits himself. We don't waste any time wiping his arse. We had other things to do. Ray bags his keys and we set out on an unlocking spree. The first to be let out are Wilkins, Payne, Davies, Turner and O'Brien, and they are out of their peters like shots from a pump-gun.

The plan is to unlock as many prisoners as we can. I get busy on one side of the landing, Ray takes the other side. I come to Ken Lawrence's cell and unlock him.

'Want to have it away, Ken?'

'Cor, not fucking much, Joe.'

'Right, See you down below.'

The next one is Lionel Galloway. He's a big blonde fellow, a fraudsman who's facing charges on a million pound credit card swindle for which he was later to get eight years. He's very bright and doesn't need to be told what to do. He's off down the stairs like a flash to join the others. I carry on with the job. Every peter I come to I say 'If you want to have it away, get downstairs', and the looks on some of the faces have to be seen to be believed. There were no refusals until I came to de Buriatte,

This was the bloke who only that afternoon has been telling me that he will make one in an escape. I unlock him and stand in the doorway.

'Coming George? We're off,' I say.

He backs into a corner away from me and starts screaming. 'Bang me up, bang me up. Put the bolt on.' Hello, I think, here's one who's lost his arsehole, but that's his business. I bang him up and carry on. I can still hear him shouting, which worries me because sound carries a long way in the huge open spaces of a prison wing. But time is getting on. Ray and I call a halt to the unlocking and go down to the ground floor.

It's a strange sight. All the geezers who have been so unexpectedly freed are standing around as if they are waiting for a coach to take them away. Some of them are wearing overcoats and sheepskins and carrying all their personal belongings, radios, books, bundles of letters and case papers. One bloke has got an enormous cardboard box full of canteen gear, tins of fruit, chocolate, biscuits and tea bags. Maybe he thinks there is a famine on outside.

Ray nudges me and points towards the main door leading to the other wings. Lionel Galloway has been told to stand there and claim any screws who happen to come through. He's dressed to kill, smart suit, silk tie and highly-polished shoes, and he's wearing a stocking mask over his face. We nearly piss ourselves laughing.

The next step is to capture the security room. This is the nerve-centre of the prison. The communication sets carried by the screws pass through the control panel there, and a direct line to the Old Bill is part of the installation. That's as much as we know about the place, apart from its location. We tell the mob to be quiet, and Ray and myself creep to the gate which leads on to a passage and then on to the security room. Very gently I turn the key in the lock on the gate and we both go on tip-toe down the passage.

We reach the room and barge in. There's a Principal Officer sitting in front of the control panel. As he jumps up and makes a dive for the alarm I give him a left hook, which puts him out, but we don't notice a screw sitting right behind the door.

He has it away sharpish down the passage, and he's moving so fast that his impetus carries him right through the waiting crowd of potential escapers.

According to Chris, who tells me about it later, Leroy Davies takes off after the screw, with Kenny Lawrence and Obie O'Brien right behind him. Leroy jumps on the screw's back, but the fellow keeps going. The screws from B wing have heard the racket, and open the gate just as the four men reach it. They all go through in a tangle of arms and legs. A screw bangs up the gate and locks it, so we not only lose three members of the gang, the scream has gone up.

Meanwhile, Ray and me are busy wrecking the security room. The various plugs and wires mean nothing to us, so we rip the lot out. There's a lot of banging and flashing and clouds of smoke, in the midst of which the PO I had hit slides through the door and gets away. It seems only a moment later that Chris Wilkins rushes in, with Richie Payne and Harry Turner right behind him.

'It's on top, Joe,' he yells.

'Where's the others?' I ask.

'Scarpering back to their peters,' says Chris,

In all the confusion on the wing, I reckon we won't be missed for some time. I sign for the others to follow me and unlock the gate leading from the wing to the kitchen. We move quickly and quietly to the kitchen door.

'Straight in and claim the screw,' I tell my mates. I silently turn the key, leaving the door closed, then it's one, two, three and in. We cop for the screw and shove him against the wall, telling him to put his hands on his head and keep still. There are three cons in the kitchen party making the tea. They stand flabbergasted with their mouths hanging open.

Padlocked to the wall is a lightweight extension ladder. We don't have a key, but Richie has something just as good. He wraps his huge hands round the padlock and twists it off. As he is performing, I see out of the corner of my eye that the screw is edging along the wall towards the alarm. I let out a shout.

'Chris - shove that fucker in the fridge.'

The screw goes white. 'No, no, don't do that. I'll freeze to death in there,' he cries.

'Just jump up and down,' I tell him as Chris bundles him into the fridge and slams the door.

I turn to the three cons, who still don't seem to realise what is happening.

'We're going over the wall,' I say. 'Any of you want to come?'

They all three shake their heads.

'Right,' I say. 'Give us five minutes, then let cookie out of the fridge.'

I grab one end of the ladder and Richie takes the other end. Ray, with a remark that it might come in useful, cops for a fire extinguisher. We come out of the kitchen by a door that leads directly into the grounds and the wall is right in front of us.

It's like stepping out on to the stage of the Palladium. All the lights are on. Ray, who is in the lead, tests out the fire extinguisher with a quick burst in the air. He should have tested the wind first. The foam blew back, covering us with streaks of white.

It's like something out of a Mack Sennett comedy as we run down the side of the administration block, Richie and me carrying the ladder, Ray in front waving the extinguisher and Harry and Chris trotting along in the rear. Suddenly three screws with Alsatians come round the corner. As soon as they see us they let the dogs go, and they come for us. Richie and me drop the ladder and prepare for battle, but Ray waits until the hounds are almost on top of us and lets go with the extinguisher right in their muzzles. The effect is dramatic. The dogs slide to a stop, then turn and run, their tails between their legs. As they skedaddle round the corner, yelping their heads off, the screws go in pursuit.

We make for the wall well away from the reception

block. The lighting is brilliant and we are in full view of the closed circuit television cameras, but it was a safe bet that they were out of action after our performance in the security room. We run the ladder up against the wall and let it out to its full extent. I go up the rungs like a rocket. It's a seventeen foot ladder and the wall is twenty-five feet high. I can just reach the top with the tips of my fingers. Chris is right behind me and takes in the situation.

'Right, Joe, stand on my shoulders,' he yells. I feel myself being propelled upwards. I sit astride the top and reach down to give Chris a hand to join me. Between us we get the other three to the top. Now all we have to do is to drop down on the other side, which is easier said than done. About a third of the way down there is a ledge which has to be cleared.

I go first, pushing myself out to clear the ledge. As I land, the shock travels up to the top of my head. Ray follows me and, as he bends his knees to absorb the shock, his arse hits the deck, his knees smash him under the chin and his glasses fly off. Luckily I catch them. After him come Richie and Harry, both heavy men, but they land safely. Funnily enough Chris's an ex-para-trooper, does his ankle in and we have to help him along as we head for the main road.

All we need now is transport, so we decide to stop the first car that comes along. I'm hoping for something in the XJ6 line, but it turns out to be a mini. I step out into the road and hold up my hand. The car stops, Ray and I go round to the driver's side, Harry and Richie stand in front and Chris is by the passenger door. The driver is an elderly bloke and there's a woman beside him. I open the door.

'Police,' I say. 'would you mind stepping out of the car, sir? He just sits there looking at us. I can't say I blame him. Ray reaches past me and cops for the ignition key.

'Look mate,' he says, 'we're escaped prisoners. We need your car. Just come out and nobody'll get hurt.'

They are out of the car in a flash, which goes to show that it sometimes pays to be honest. We all pile in, Ray takes the wheel and we are off, leaving the old couple on the pavement in a state of total bewilderment.

A successful escape falls into three parts. First you get out, then you get away and finally you stay out. The first part had gone well. As we rolled along through the back streets towards Clapham Common, the second part of the enterprise seemed to be in order. Near the tube station I spotted a church with a large open space in front.

'OK, Ray, drive in here,' I said. Ray parked close to the wall. There was no-one about. We crawled out of the mini and, as I wriggled out of my overalls, I suddenly felt a hard lump in the pocket. I had completely forgotten that, as I left the security room, I had nicked the master key from its glass case on the wall. I hung on to it, threw the overalls in the back of the car, then followed the others as they strolled across the road to the station.

All we had between us was a fifty pence piece. I bought five tenpenny tickets and, as we walked to the escalator, we heard the sirens wailing as police cars sped to Brixton. I look at the time on the station clock. It was six fifty, just forty-five minutes since the caper had started. We made our way to the northbound platform, got in the first train that came along and sat on different seats in the same carriage. If we'd sat together it would have been noticeable.

It wasn't long before the reaction set in. Sitting opposite me is a bird in a very short skirt and, as I'm looking at her, I also catch Chris's eye. He smiled and I smiled back. Then he began to laugh and I laughed too. The other three, all in different parts of the carriage, took it up, and there we were, laughing our heads off and not quite knowing why. Laughter is infectious. Very soon most of the passengers have joined in. What we were laughing at, of course, was a vivid remembrance of some recent scenes, a couple of screws trussed up like turkeys, one of them with his pants full of shit: Lionel Galloway in his stocking mask and Saville Row suit and three Alsatian dogs falling over each other to get away from us. And above all, we were laughing because we were free.

We left the train at Charing Cross, and I made a transfer charge call, as a result of which I was told that a couple of cars would be at the Embankment entrance to the station within fifteen minutes. All of a sudden I notice that Chris is missing. Then I heard his voice. There was one of these fire-and-brimstone merchants spouting from a platform, and Chris was verballing him from the crowd. I weeded him out just as the cars arrived.

The mate who provided the cars was an old friend who owed me. I expected that we would be taken to a safe flop for the time being, but I was surprised to find that our destination was a luxurious penthouse in the heart of the West End, It was a smashing pad, deep carpets, modern furniture, colour tele, the lot. There were two birds living there, Julie and Angie, who worked as hostesses at Churchill's Club.

'Whats the score. Charlie?' I asked my mate as we made ourselves comfortable in the lounge.

'Only place I could think of, Joe,' he replied. 'Don't worry. The girls are as good as gold. It'll cost you, but I think you'll find it's worth it.'

He was minding a couple of grand for me, so I was able to see that the girls were well sweetened. Anyway they didn't seem to object to having a few husky blokes about the place. The only snag was that the rent was paid by a sugar-daddy, but he wasn't expected to turn up in the near future, so that was alright. Being five-handed we had to double up in the spare bedrooms, but it was better than being three-up in Brixton,

I went through all the papers the following morning, but they only gave brief mentions of our escape, which was quite natural, as the true story would have led to a lot of red faces at Brixton, The old couple whose car we had nicked came in for a bit of exposure, appearing on the tele and seeming to enjoy it. From what they said it appeared that they had gone along to the screws' club to report the escape, thinking it was the prison proper. One of the screws turned them away. 'Not ours, mate. They're all locked up for the night,' he told them. It was an hour of glory for the old dears, something to tell their grandchildren.

During the next couple of days news came out of the prison about what had happened after we went over the wall. For a time nobody knew that anybody had escaped at all, such was the confusion. The cons who had gone back to their cells believed that we were banged up in the chokey. It wasn't until the ten o'clock news reported that five prisoners had made a getaway that they realised that their efforts had not been in vain. They shouted and cheered, bellowing the news from the windows and banging on the doors of their cells. The only bloke who didn't do any cheering was George de Buriatte, the fucking grass, who did all he could to wreck our plan. It was a good job I hadn't let him in. This merchant later admitted in an article in 'Weekend' magazine that he had been responsible for putting more than a hundred and fifty men away.

A message came out to me via Leroy Davies' brother Glen that there was a right old fuss going on over the master key I had nicked, and Leroy, Kenny Lawrence and Obie O'Brien were having a lot of aggravation over it. The bloody thing was no use to me, but I gathered that it would go down on the credit side if the key found its way back to its rightful place on the wall of the security room. I made arrangements for it to be returned by 'special' messenger.

That same day Big Harry left us. He'd done his bit during the escape and we were really sorry to lose him. He went off to see his wife, who persuaded him to give himself up so, like the little nigger boys, now we were four, Ray, Chris, Richie and myself. Poor old Chris was in a bad way. His foot, which he had injured when he jumped from the wall, was swollen to twice its normal size and had turned all the colours of the rainbow.

We got hold of a nurse who could be trusted to keep her mouth shut, and she came round to the flat. When she examined Chris's foot she made no bones about it. He had smashed his ankle and needed hospital care. That being out of the question, she bandaged the foot and packed ice bags round it to reduce the swelling and ease the pain.

'He ought to have a crutch', she said.

I volunteered the information that he already had one, and anyhow it was his foot we were worried about, not his balls.

'That's the sort of remark I would expect from you', she said. 'I mean a crutch to help him walk'.

'So where do we get a crutch?' asks Richie

'Knowing you lot, you'd probably snatch it from a cripple in the street,' she said.

That afternoon Richie and me set out to capture a

crutch. Richie is at the wheel of Angie's little Ford. We have already decided that it would be too risky to march into John, Bell and Croydon's and buy one, because there might have been some awkward questions, so we make our way to Westminster Hospital. Richie parked the car and we strolled in. As things turned out we could have nicked the bloody hospital, because we were never challenged. I picked up a white coat which was hanging about doing nothing and slipped it on. The transformation was amazing. Now I looked like a thug in a white coat.

We roam around the corridors and finally we spot it, a lovely aluminium crutch sitting on a trolley waiting to be captured. I picked it up and, with Richie at my side doing a crutch salesman act, we walked out of the door past the porter and were gone.

I slung the crutch into the back of the car.

'OK, Rich,' I said. 'There's no rush now. Let's have a little drive round.'

Richie was just as keen as me to see the sights, but as we swung into Victoria Street, Richie glanced in the mirror.

'Heads up, Joe. It's the filth,' he said.

'Where ?'

'Right up our arse.'

I looked back, and there was the Old Bill right behind us. 'Keep going, Richie I said. I leaned back and shifted the crutch which was lying on the back seat, making sure they got a good eyeful. It's as if I was saying 'You wouldn't nick a cripple, would you?'. It didn't have any effect. They followed us round Parliament Square and up towards Westminster Bridge. Just after we had crossed the lights by the Houses of Parliament I spotted an opening on the left. 'Turn in here and keep going' I said.

Richie dutifully did as he was told, and the Old Bill followed us as though their car was tied to ours with a piece of string. Suddenly I realised where we were. The opening we had turned into was Cannon Row, and we were in Scotland Yard.

'Hold it, Richie,' I said. 'Just do a quiet U-turn and go back.'

The police car stopped and the two occupants watched us as we drove slowly past to join the bridge-bound traffic. They made no move to follow us. Richie turned left on to the Embankment.

'Jesus Christ,' I said. 'I thought they'd sussed us.'

Richie came up with a classic reply.

'Maybe they don't read the papers,' he said.

We stayed at the flat for a couple of weeks or so, and it wasn't bad. Chris's foot was mending slowly and we had all we wanted in the way of food and booze. Occasionally Julie and Angie brought some mates back from the club, so we didn't want for the other. One night Ray, Richie and myself were watching tele when we heard a loud, regular knocking. We dived out of our chairs convinced that it was on top until we realised that the noise was coming from one of the bedrooms. We crept down the hallway and opened the door to find Julie and Chris performing. They were going at it so hard that the headboard was banging on the wall.

CHAPTER TWELVE

JOE:

It is Monday the 9th of June 1972, and the time is a little after eleven o'clock in the morning. A silver-blue Ford Corsair saloon 2000E is speeding along Cranbrook Road in Ilford. E is for 'Executive', but there is nothing of the executive about the four men in the car. They are not wearing striped suits but their faces are covered by striped scarves, worn balaclava fashion and with eyeholes cut in them.

Chris Wilkins is at the wheel. The other three occupants are Richard 'Honeypuff' Payne, Ray 'Scarface' Pegler and myself. We are on our way to make a withdrawal from the National Westminster Bank, Ilford branch, of a substantial sum of money. None of us have cheque books, but Scarface and myself are carrying sawn-off shotguns and Honeypuff is armed with a pickaxe. Chris makes a tyre-screaming turn into Beehive Lane, goes left and slams the car up on to the pavement outside the bank. He stays at the wheel and we three leap out and burst through the doors. I shout 'Don't anybody move. This is a raid', and make for the security door with Honeypuff right behind me. Scarface stays by the door and orders the customers to lie on the floor face down. Some of them don't seem too willing to do this, but Scarface waggles the shotgun at them and they go down.

The security door is locked, so I shout 'Open this fucking door or you'll get shot'. It's opened in double-quick time and me and Honeypuff get behind the counter. Somebody has pressed the silent alarm which is connected directly to the local nick. This action also closes and locks the cash drawers. I point the shotgun at the cashiers and order them to lie on the floor. Honeypuff goes to work with the pickaxe, forces open the drawers and loads the cash into a white bag. There's a sudden commotion at the main door. A woman is walking in, looking over her shoulder at the car parked up on the pavement. She turns, sees Scarface and lets out a scream, but she's soon down on the floor with the rest of the customers. Honeypuff has captured the loot. He goes through the security door and I back out with the sawn-off at the ready. We meet up with Scarface at the main door. There is a loud shout from one of the geezers behind the counter.

'You've missed most of it,' he yells.

He's wrong. We're well pleased with what we've got. We sprint to the car and pile in, Chris lets the clutch out and makes a quick U-turn. Down Cranbrook Road we go like an arrow from a bow. We ditch the Corsair in Dersingham Road at Manor Park and switch to another car, then drive slowly back to the flat. Honeypuff tips the bag out on to the floor, the carpet is covered in readies.

'Not bad, eh?' he laughs.

'Did you cop for that feller,' says Scarface, 'You haven't got it all, he says. That's the slippery bastard who set off the alarm.'

We go out shopping that afternoon. There's a gaff in Shepherd Street called Quincy's and Ray, Chris and me have a walk round, looking at the gear. We get the odd look from one of the salesmen, and the next thing we know somebody has slipped round behind us and locked the door. We give each other the nod, If there's any move to the 'phone we go out straight through the plate-glass door.

We've picked up a few articles, so we go to the counter and pay for them, something like eighty-odd quid. The bloke who had locked the door slyly unlocks it and we leave the premises. It would have been a bit of an anti-climax, being nicked as shoplifters after doing a bank.

Later on that evening we sat round the television having a drink. Ray had gone out to meet a mate of his, and we were just discussing going clubbing when the ten o'clock news came on. I don't remember which talking head it was, but I very well remember what it said.

'One of the men who escaped from Brixton Prison a few weeks ago was re-captured earlier this evening after a brief car chase through the West End of London. The man, Raymond Pegler, was recognised by a police officer on routine car patrol'.

The news was a bit of a facer. Ray was driving an MG with a distinctive number plate. It had been parked outside the building on several occasions, and may have been spotted by the Old Bill, in which case they would be on to us. Also, though it wasn't likely, Ray might have been carrying a letter or something that would give a clue to our whereabouts. We knew one thing for certain. Ray wouldn't grass us up. We decided to get out of the flat right away and meet next day at Valerie Cable's flat over in Halley Road, the other side of Stratford. We packed our gear and cleared out.

It was about quarter past three in the afternoon when I arrived at Val's place. It was a nice roomy flat on the upper floor of a Victorian house. Chris and Richie had already arrived, and Val was brewing up in the kitchen.

I had hardly sat down when the telephone rang and Val went to answer it. She picked up the receiver, held it to her ear for a few moments, then replaced it.

'What was that, Val?' I said.

'Oh, some nutter,' she replied. 'Didn't say anything. Just rang off.'

I jumped from the chair and picked up the receiver. As I thought, the line was dead. Whoever had rung hadn't replaced the receiver at the other end. It was a typical Old Bill trick to prevent a call being made out when they were ready to move in. I went to the window and looked out, and sure enough the street below was swarming with law, about five or six cars and a couple of vans and Old Bill with rifles and shooters all over the place.

I turned to the others. 'Quick, it's on fucking top,' I yelled. As Chris and Richie make a dive for the bedroom I dash into the kitchen. I have a few grand on me in readies, which I stuff into an empty chocolate box and drop into the rubbish bin. A big voice booms out from downstairs.

'We are armed police officers. We have a warrant to search this house. Stay where you are.'

As Val went out to the head of the stairs I made for the loft, threw back the cover and climbed up. From my hiding place I heard the Old Bill rush into the flat and drag Chris and Richie out of the bedroom. I knew it was only a matter of time before my turn came, and I was dead right. 'You in the loft. You've got a minute to come out before we fire through the ceiling.'

I had no chance. I pulled the cover to one side and lowered myself ready to drop. As I did so, one of the armed coppers smashed the butt of his rifle against my ankle and I fell to the floor. I was in agony.

'Tut, tut. You shouldn't have done that, officer,' said the Detective Inspector who was in charge of the raid. He was laughing all over his face.

'I thought he was going to run away, sir,' said the

rozzer, smiling happily,

All I could think of was getting downstairs where there would at least be a crowd of bystanders to witness any further brutality. I closed my eyes and pretended to faint. I was dragged out by a couple of heavyweights to a waiting car and ended up in West Ham nick. The DI, whose name was East, and another officer travelled with me in the car.

I have always held to the rule that it's best to say nothing after a nicking, but I had to get one thing straight.

'You'll find there's some money in a chocolate box in the kitchen - in the rubbish bin,' I told East, 'It's down to me.'

'Oh, really,' said East, 'Part of your share of the loot?'

'Don't know what you're talking about, guv'nor. It's my life savings.'

'So what's it doing in the rubbish bin?'

'I always hide my money there. Lot of thieves about,'

East laughed, It didn't really matter what I said, it would come out his way in the verbal. All I was worried about was that it shouldn't be down to Chris or Richie, As it turned out, the bin wasn't searched until about two hours later by a pair of DS's from the Regional Crime Squad. They called in a neighbour of Val's, a chap called Rider, and counted the cash there in front of him. Three grand had shrunk to two hundred and eighty five pounds. Something like two thousand seven hundred had gone missing.

Actually the scoundrels had done me a favour. The less money found, the greater my chances of getting away on a charge of robbery.

Later that day we were taken to Ilford nick. Chris, Richie and me were charged with robbery and receiving.

My troubles weren't over yet. Out of the blue came a DI from Paddington to interview me about a Mrs. Clarke who had been assaulted and robbed in Bayswater earlier in the year. I copped for that one too. It never rains but it pours. Chris and me were taken to Ilford Hospital to receive attention for our respective injured ankles. Needless to say, we were heavily escorted. Then the doctor asked me how I had received the injury I told him that a copper had whacked me with the butt of a rifle. He turned to one of the coppers.

'Is that true?' he asked.

'No, sir,' came the reply. 'He fell off the wall at Brixton. There are no prizes for guessing whose explanation was accepted.

At the Magistrates' Court hearing we are remanded in custody. I didn't need a vivid imagination to envisage what kind of a reception was awaiting us at Brixton. We had tied up a couple of screws, locked another one in the fridge and I had personally chinned a Principal Officer. It was a safe bet that somebody was going to be hurt, and we were in the frame as prime favourites.

We had an escort worthy of a Prime Minister going to address a meeting of unemployed. We went into the reception area, Chris and I leaning on each other's shoulders with only two good legs between us. There were far more screws about than was usual, and it looked as though it was going to be off. The escort handed us over, our property was checked and we were told to lead on through the tunnel that led to the second reception and the baths.

This was where it would happen, and I clenched my fists in anticipation. I had made up my mind that I was going to fight. As I came to the end of the tunnel, a screw was standing there. As I passed him I saw him out of the corner of my eye as he raised his hand. I swung round, ready to ride the blow and reply in kind, but all I get is a friendly pat on the back.

'Well done, Cannon,' he says.

I couldn't believe my own ears. When I heard him say the same words to Chris and Richie, I was even more flabbergasted. There were a dozen screws waiting at the desk which was normally manned by a single officer. They were laughing and cracking jokes.

'Right, you buggers, you won't get away this time.'

'We've got you taped.'

'No more birds and booze now, eh?'

There were many similar comments but not one of them raised a hand against us. Thinking it over, I reckoned that they had a sneaking admiration for us and didn't want to add to our troubles by coming the heavy, which they could quite easily have done. It was one of those cases of let bygones be bygones but we'll make sure you don't do it again.

The surprising thing was that we received no punishment at all for the escape attempt. We were brought before the Governor and were later interviewed by the Brixton police to answer a lot of questions to which we gave a load of rubbish in reply. We were put on special watch, with two screws on constant guard outside our doors, but other than that we were treated as ordinary remand cases.

Ray Pegler told us details of how he was captured. He was upset in case we thought that he had grassed us, but we put him right on that score. Some of the other blokes we had unlocked gave us full marks for trying, so all in all we didn't come out of it badly. There was one little matter that I saw to personally. I had a chat with de Buriatte and made sure he understood that I disapproved of his behaviour on the night of the escape. He got the message.

I settled down into the routine very quickly. I had no more thoughts of escaping. All I had to worry about was facing the charges against me, and that was quite enough. My first appearance before a judge and jury was on the burglary charge in connection with the garage from which I had run the mini-cab business, but I was assured by my brief that the evidence against me was pretty flimsy and I stood a good chance of getting chucked. Consequently, when I went up the steps at the Inner London Sessions I was quite cheerful.

One of the nice things about the British judicial system is that the accused can, within reason, call as many defence witnesses as he likes. I told my brief that certain persons now being held in Brixton were essential witnesses, so Chris, Richie, Ray Pegler, Leroy Davies and a couple of other merchants found themselves having a day out and a decent lunch which I had arranged to be sent in to them. Of course, they weren't called, they just sat around chatting and smoking.

The case didn't take long. Andy the Greek and his lousy brother-in-law weren't very convincing in the witness box and the judge quite properly slung the case out. That didn't mean that I left the dock without a stain on my character to emerge into the outside world as a free man. I returned to Brixton to await the next development in the Cannon saga.

In November I was at the Old Bailey before Judge Edward Clarke on a charge of robbing Mrs Clarke (no relation to His Lordship) of money and jewellery. The judge was no stranger to me. He was the one who sent me down on the pub affair, when I appeared with the Mills brothers and Charlie Canavan, so my card was marked so far as he was concerned. I have the sort of face that is not easily forgotten.

The chief police witness was a Detective Inspector Ridley, a bent copper who was later, in 1982, sentenced to twelve months on corruption charges. He comes out with a load of verbal about my having been a drinking companion of the lady, which she denies very strongly, and also says that I made an oral confession to him in West Ham nick, which is a load of rubbish. He overstepped the mark when he rabbited on about Valerie Cable 'being brought into the nick by DS Hayday of the Regional Crime Squad, thus linking me with the Ilford job' before I had even been tried. Anyway, it made no odds, the damage had been done and I was weighed off with four years.

Goodbye Brixton and the privileges of sent-in meals and unlimited canteen facilities. I was carted off to Wandsworth, rigged out in yellow patches and put on the A list. What this amounts to is that I am issued a book with my photo and description which is handed to the screw in charge of me at any given time. He was responsible for me until he handed me over to some other screw. This served a double purpose. If I managed to get away it would be a miracle, secondly the prison authorities would have somebody to jump on in case I did escape.

In some ways being an A man had its advantages. They were always at the head of the queue when it came to seeing the Governor or the doctor or the welfare. On the other hand, security in the mailbag shop was very tight and the precautions taken on exercise had to be experienced to be believed. I never knew when I was going to go walkies until a screw came into the shop and read my name out. Then there was the irritation of special searches when a con could be stopped at any time and given a rub-down.

It was one of these special searches that landed me in trouble. A chap called Jackie Jury, who later died in Hull, was carrying more snout than he was entitled to when the two screws who carried out these searches turned up in the mailbag shop. He got the wind up. I was right next to him.

'What shall I do, Joe?' he said out of the corner of his mouth.

'Go for a piss and ditch it,' I said.

One of the search screws, a very nasty specimen who wasn't very fond of me, noticed that I was talking. 'You, face the front and shut up,' he said. I took the chance to create a diversion, which would give Jackie a chance to get rid of the snout. 'Who the fucking hell do you think you're talking to,' I said. 'You dressed-up prick. I've eaten better things than you before breakfast.'

All I wanted to do was take the screw's attention away from Jackie, but it went wrong. The screw dived for the alarm bell and the heavy mob was on the scene in no time. They claimed me and frog-marched me out of the shop. I went quietly, it wasn't worth starting a fight, but the screw who'd sent up the scream had other ideas. As I was hustled down to the chokey he walked behind me and suddenly kicked me in the kidneys. As I turn round the heavy mob take this as a gesture of defiance. They rushed me into a cell and really set about me.

I didn't fight back. I could have claimed two or three of them, but that would have given them a holiday with pay on so-called sick leave and I would have to face the serious charge of assaulting a prison officer. I covered up and yelled blue bloody murder as the sticks and boots came in, and after a while they gave up. I was black and blue all over and had to have medical attention, but it could have been worse.

The next day I was up before the Governor and made a formal complaint, but he refused to accept it unless it was in writing. I had nothing to lose. My written complaint was considered by the Visiting Magistrates, who referred it back to the Governor with a recommendation that I should be punished for making false and malicious accusations. The Deputy Governor then refers it to the next lot of Visiting Magistrates, who found me not guilty of the offence. The substance of the allegations, that I had been savagely beaten, were shoved on one side. Over the coming years I was to fight for the right to take action in the civil courts against the bastards who had hammered me. All I got from the authorities was delay, prevarication and outright obstruction.

All screws aren't tarred with the same brush. The majority are quite decent fellows who do a difficult job to the best of their ability. It's the minority of spineless shits who cause the bother. Delve into the causes of the riots at Hull, Chelmsford, Parkhurst and other prisons and somewhere along the line is a small group of bullying psychopaths dressed in prison officers' uniform who, instead of being weeded out, are protected by authority in the name of prison discipline. They treat men like animals, brutalise them and subject them to all sorts of humiliation. Complaints against them are disregarded. No wonder the wretched con reaches a point where he says 'Fuck it' and takes the law into his own hands.

By April of '73, conditions had become so bad in Wandsworth that the prisoners were in a mood verging on open rebellion, particularly as regards the 'no talking' rule. Individual complaints to the Governor proved useless, so twenty-one cons made application to him for the order to be relaxed. I was one of them. The next thing I knew, I was up before the Governor and put on Rule 43, solitary segregation for the good order and discipline of the prison. I was the only one singled out for this treatment which went on for seven months, the only break being the few days I spent at the Old Bailey when I stood trial for the Ilford Bank job.

There were three of us standing in the dock, Chris Wilkins and Richie Payne being the other two. Valerie Cable should have been there with us but she was in hospital after having taken an overdose of sleeping tablets, a piece of codology to 'help our defence. Ray Pegler was safely tucked up in jail somewhere, and the best of British to him.

The outcome of the trial was in no doubt. We were all marked down for hefty doses of porridge, so it was just a matter of going through the motions, and some of the proceedings would have made a cat laugh. DI Ridley, the Paddington terror, had a field day in the witness box with pages of verbal along the lines of 'fair cop, guv' and 'you got me bang to rights', the sort of phoney dialogue used by TV writers which bear no relation to the real language of villains. He went into a song and dance about bringing Valerie Cable to the West Ham nick, saying he was led to do so by 'humane considerations'. My brief caught him out in palpable lies more than once.

Another comic turn was DS Hayday of the Regional Crime Squad, who came up with such gems as 'I'm no snout', a term used to describe a grass by the Bow Street runners. Chris, said Hayday, came up with ' if you've got any witnesses, let's get on with the IDs (identification parades). I was well masked'. I looked at Chris, he looked at me and we both had to laugh. Then Richie pulls one out of the bag with evidence that he was in Austin Reeds in Knightsbridge at the same time as the bank was being done in Ilford, We all knew where he was, including the filth, but they couldn't prove it.

My brief called the copper who had smashed my ankle with the butt of his rifle.

'How did Cannon come by the injury to his ankle? ' asked the brief.

'Escaping from Brixton prison, sir,' says the idiot.

Previous evidence had proved that the robber presumed to be Cannon had been leaping about like a gazelle in the course of the raid. Even members of the jury had to smile at this barefaced piece of fiction.

Eventually the trial came to an end. To our surprise Richie got chucked and walked from the court a free man. The jury, by a majority verdict, convicted Chris and me of receiving but not guilty of robbery, which shows what they thought of the way the prosecution handled the case. It also indicated their opinion of the comic act Ridley and Hayday, but, though the jury decides guilt or innocence, it's the judge who does the sentencing. Despite the gaping holes in the evidence and the comic opera nature of the trial, he gave me eight years and awarded seven to Chris.

I am sure that, had it not been for the silly copper who said I had done my ankle at Brixton, I would have been found guilty of robbery. Also I think that the jury did not take kindly to being treated like a bunch of half-wits in being asked to believe the verbal garbage introduced by Ridley and Hayday. I remember reading that Lord Kilbrandon, addressing the International Commission of Jurists in 1976, said that 'the verbal is becoming a music hall joke'. He must have read the transcripts of the trial of Payne, Wilkins and Cannon.

It was back once more to Wandsworth and solitary. I must say I missed the daily trip to to the Bailey, where I had at least been able to talk to somebody. Now I could only talk to myself. I put up the best performance possible in these one-sided conversations, but I found it hard to laugh at my own jokes. I'd heard them all before. On a serious note, while I don't recommend solitary as a life-style, except for Trappist monks, it does exercise the old thinking machinery. There's not much else to do.

One morning, right out of the blue, I was told to pack up my belongings as I was being moved to another prison. I didn't bother to ask where I was going. Anywhere must be better than Wandsworth. Eventually, after some shuttling around, I ended up in Chelmsford; a place about thirty-odd miles from London with a cathedral, a golf course and a museum. There was also a prison which isn't mentioned in the guide books.

I was quite wary as I walked into reception. As a potential escaper I was well escorted and my A list status would be well-known to the prison staff. My surprise can be imagined when the reception screw stuck his hand out.

'Hello, Cannon,' he said. 'No hard feelings, eh.'

I wondered what the hell he was talking about. I had seen him somewhere before but I couldn't quite place him. He saw that I was puzzled.

'The last time I saw you, you were tying me up in Brixton' he said.

It all came back to me then, and I felt a bit of a shit. Here was this merchant who had it in his power to make things tough for me and get his own back, and he was holding out his hand. As I've said before, not all screws are bastards. I took the hand and shook it heartily.

'Look,' I said, 'I'm sorry about that. You know how it is.

'Sure, I know. All water under the bridge now, isn't it.'

I was choked. Later on, when I got to know him better, he turned out to be a first class bloke, and he did me many a favour during my stay.

It's a small world and full of coincidences . The following day, under escort, I was allowed to watch a match being played on the football field, quite a treat for me after my stretch in Wandsworth where all I had seen was a wired-in exercise yard. There was a bloke in civvies standing on the touchline near me. It was 'Mad Mike' Selby, who ran the Rugby Club in Notting Dale when I was a kid. I thought he must be a member of the staff, because he obviously wasn't a con.

'Hello, Mad Mike,' I said. 'How are you?' I could see he was trying to figure out who I was.

'Joe Cannon, from Notting Dale, Nobby's young brother,' I said.

'Oh, yes. I remember,' he said. His manner was a bit frosty.

'What are you doing here?' I asked.

He gave a slight grin. 'You'll find out on Monday morning,' he said, nodded and walked off. This was Saturday afternoon. On the Monday morning I was on parade outside the Governor's office. This was usual procedure.Only the Governor or his deputy sees every new inmate as soon after arrival as possible, but only on weekdays. I had been delivered on Friday afternoon. As usual I was at the head of the queue, and marched in with a couple of screws in close attendance. Sitting behind the desk, a Principal Officer at his elbow, was 'Mad Mike', now the Governor of HM Prison, Chelmsford. I'm not the blushing type but, when I thought of the way I had greeted him, was my face red.

He acted as though he had never been on the football field on Saturday. I don't see how he could have done otherwise, but when he was delivering the stock speech about being a good boy, obeying rules, keeping out of trouble and so on, there was a little twinkle in his eye. I was duly marched out, but I think he must have had a word with the PO, because I didn't have any of the aggro which happens to an A man when he changes prisons. Actually, I was surprised at the amount of freedom I was given. The rules were carried out to the letter, but it was the interpretation of those rules which made my life easier.

To a tough nut who had taken Dartmoor, Wandsworth and even Rampton in his stride, Chelmsford was a piece of cake, notwithstanding the category A label. I settled down there quite nicely and got myself involved with an organisation inside the prison which called itself Recidivists Anonymous. They produced a regular magazine with official sanction, but it was only for circulation within the confines of the jail and was subject to censorship, so it was a pretty weak-kneed effort. I wrote a few articles and helped in the production, which gave me something to do in my spare time.

I don't really know why I suddenly upset the applecart. On the whole the screws were a decent bunch, so I suppose it was just bad luck that the one who stopped me outside my cell was one of the few bastards. He had a sneering look on his face and a lot of venom in his voice.

'Pack your gear, Cannon,' he said. 'You're changing cells'

I'd put in a lot of work on the peter, scrubbing the table and chair, keeping the floor clean and sticking up a few pictures on the walls, so I wasn't keen on moving, and really the only reason for the move was the rule that said an A man's cell should be changed from time to time.

'Come off it, mate,' I said. 'I like this peter.'

'Say 'sir' when you speak to me, And don't fucking argue, you cunt,' he said.

That did it. I stuck one on his chops, which took the sneer off his face, but a couple of other screws joined in. For a moment I thought of chucking the towel in, but then I thought of Wandsworth and how far I didn' t get by going through the 'proper channels', so I steamed in and soon had the three of them in trouble. By the time the heavy mob came up at the double, I had decked two of them and was just putting the finishing touches to the third. Then the big stick started swinging and that was my lot.

I went through the rigmarole of chokey, Visiting Magistrates, loss of remission and fourteen days loss of privileges, in fact loss of everything except my self respect. The three screws went on extended sick leave on full pay, and I went on the transfer list, destination Parkhurst prison on the Isle of Wight.

I don't think it has much to do with anything but a few months later HM Prison, Chelmsford, was burned to the ground. As I remember, whoever or whatever caused the blaze remained a mystery.

CHAPTER THIRTEEN

JOE:

All prisons are bad news but, apart from Dartmoor, the gaggle of ugly buildings just outside Newport on the Isle of Wight rank very low on the list of Her Majesty's holiday camps.

There are three penal establishments in the huge complex. Camp Hill is a red-brick victorian prison which was at one time a Borstal, now used to house short-term young prisoners. Albany is a more modern place entirely, equipped with all the latest and most up-to-date contrivances for cutting off the malefactor from contact with the outside world. Parkhurst proper is the ugly sister of the trio, an ancient mausoleum of crumbling brick steadily falling to pieces as a result of the ravages of time and the regular convict riots.

There were three of us in the green coach that left Wandsworth, where I had spent the night in transit. The designers of the coach must have been under the impression that prisoners have specially sprung arses, because there was no padding on the seats. The screws were wise to that. They brought their own cushions. At Portsmouth the coach was driven on to the ferry that plied between the mainland and the Isle of Wight and there we were, a sort of peep-show, firmly manacled to the seats.

I've never been much of a seaman, and I wasn't looking forward to this trip across the choppy waters of the Solent. To begin with, the ferry was an old tub with flat ends, not the most efficient design for a smooth passage through water. Also the engines weren't up to much, they seemed to be doing their best to shake the vessel to pieces. What with the constant vibration and the crashing of the waves against the flat bows I was beginning to get a bit panicky.

'What about taking these cuffs off, guv?' I said to one of the screws. 'If this fucking heap goes down we've had it.'

'You'll be alright, Cannon, It won't go down. If it does, I'm a good swimmer.'

You'd better be, mate, I thought, because if anything does go wrong I'll cling to you like a fucking leech. Anyway, nothing did go wrong and, twenty minutes after leaving the ferry, we were being driven through the forbidding gates of Parkhurst. I went through the reception routine, including a vigorous search by the reception screws known as the 'burglars'. I don't know what they expected to find, as I had just come from Wandsworth, which isn't exactly a freedom centre. I was then allocated to A wing, where I had my first shock.

The wing was a shithouse, it looked like one and it smelled like one. The floor tiles, alternate red and black, were cracked and broken. The so-called paintwork was filthy and what lighting there was came from unshaded and flyblown low-wattage bulbs.

The interiors of the cells were indescribable. Those which had been recently occupied were cleaner than the rest, but in the majority they weren't fit for pigs. Pigeons had flown in through the broken windows and built their nests, there was birdshit all over the floors, rats, mice and cockroaches abounded and the wooden floors on the upper landings were full of woodworm.

I was lucky enough to meet a couple of old friends as entered the wing. They knew the ropes and helped me to wangle a decent cell and some furniture. One of them was Bertie Edwards, who I had first met years before in

Dartmoor. He was in his late forties and a fitness fanatic, wearing shorts and singlet whatever the weather and dead keen on weight-lifting. The other was Patsy Fleming, one of the old school of villains, who had escaped from Nottingham in 1955 along with Alfie Hinds. He was doing eight years for a wage snatch at a South London printing firm, but what Patsy didn't know was that the Old Bill had been tipped off that it was to be an armed raid. He was most upset when his car was fired on. He didn't believe in shooters. Bertie, on the other hand, had no such scruples. Part of his ten stretch was awarded for firearms offences. Shooters or not, it made little difference. We all landed up in the same place.

Come teatime I was in trouble. I should explain that I had been having pains in my stomach for about three years, and had been on what is known as 'gastric diet' in Brixton, Wandsworth and Chelmsford. A prisoner's diet, like his record, follows him wherever he goes, but the machinery had gone wrong somewhere down the line. I presented myself at the serving counter. 'Cannon, gastric,' I said.

'Not here, mate, you're not,' said the screw. 'Our gastric cases are in the hospital. You have what everybody else has or you go without.'

I went without, not only then but for the next two days. On the third day I turned up to collect the evening meal.

'Finished the hunger-strike then,' said the screw.

I didn't reply. I took the plate of greasy rubbish and marched into the Principal Officer's room.

'I can't eat this, sir,' I said. 'I'm supposed to be on gastric diet.'

'It's that or nothing,' said the PO. 'If you're sick, put down for the doctor.'

My guts were giving me hell and all this rabbit wasn't helping. On a sudden impulse I slung the plate of grub at him, and that was me down the chokey in double-quick time. I had a visit from the heavy mob.

'We tame lions in here, Cannon,' said the leader. 'How do you want it? Rough or smooth?'

I never felt less like fighting, and they cleared off. When I came up before the Governor the following day I was awarded seven days punishment, which was no sort of a cure for whatever was wrong with me, in fact I felt very much worse. When I came out of chokey I was transferred to B wing and put on a diet which mainly consisted of milk and crackers with additions from the normal menu. You've made a fine start in Parkhurst, I said to myself.

B wing was relatively small and contained some very peculiar prisoners, not real nutters, just funny. A few were there at their own request, preferring the privacy of a small wing, but there were others, not very nice people, sex offenders and known grasses who were there for their own protection. The regime was different too. On the other wings they were unlocked at 6.45 am and not locked up again until 9.00 pm, but on B wing there was much more rattling of keys and banging of doors. It was collect breakfast, lock up till 8, collect lunch at 11.45, lock up till 1.00, collect tea at 5.00, lock up till 5.45, after which the prisoner can spend his time in association until 9.00 or remain banged up. I never fathomed out the reason for this wear and tear on the twirls, unless it was a cute psychological trick to ensure that the con did not forget that he was in a prison. As if we were likely to.

There wasn't a lot to do outside the cells. There were two television rooms, one table tennis set, another room for card players and a library about the size of a council

210

house toilet. A part of the ground floor was partitioned off to provide the punishment block. On the landings, the recesses were a fine example of neglect and decay, lavatory doors either missing completely or hanging from the hinges, no seats to the toilets and wash basins torn away from the walls. It was all very depressing.

The rule book says that every prisoner will be allocated to work for which he is most suited. There were no vacancies for minders, ex-drinking club owners or bank robbers, so I was put in the Press shop which turns out such things as Army mess tins, ash trays, cash boxes and the like. Actually, work allocation was a joke. I came across fully-qualified electrician banging rivets into mess can handles while lorry drivers were put to work as electricians mates. A fully trained fireman worked in the laundry, but the red-band, a 'trusted prisoner', who was in charge of the fire party was a musician.

The noise in the shop was deafening, ancient presses which should by rights be on the scrap-heap banging away in competition with the rattle of the overhead belt drive mechanism. There was no need to enforce a no-talking rule. The only means of communication was by sign language. Next door the Fab (short for fabrication) shop was a comparative haven of peace and quiet as lines of workers fitted together the bits and pieces churned out by the presses.

It was in these shops, where offensive weapons were ready to hand in the shape of hammers and other tools, that most of the incidents of violence took place.

There was a little chap working in the Fab shop, a coloured merchant seaman serving life for killing the captain of his ship. From his appearance one would have thought that he wasn't capable of killing a fly. He got into an argument with another prisoner, who made the mistake of turning his back to walk away. The seaman picked up a hammer from the bench and let the other fellow have it just behind the ear. With the hammer sticking out of his skull, the victim tried to get to his feet several times, but fell over at each attempt. The blow had destroyed that portion of his brain which controlled his balance. He was transferred to the hospital at Winchester, and I believe his condition remains unchanged to this day.

There were many other incidents of a similar kind, but what stood out a mile was that the attacker seemed to to be intent on killing his victim, not just harming him. Also the causes of these incidents were, in the main, trivial. An ill-judged remark or a quarrel over a few penceworth of tobacco is hardly worth a life. In America they call it 'stir crazy', this madness which drives men who have been locked up for years and treated like animals to a point where they commit murder.

I arrived at Parkhurst shortly before the festive season, but Christmas in prison is no cake-walk, if you'll forgive the pun. It was a pretty sad and miserable time for the family men and it's not exactly a bundle of fun for the others. We all got an extra twenty pence from the Common Fund to spend on riotous living, and the food on Christmas Day and Boxing Day was an improvement on the usual fare, which was diabolical by any standards. We did get to see a couple of fairly up-to-date films, 'The Sting' and 'The Three Musketeers', but that was the extent of the jollification.

After the so-called celebrations it was business as usual, and the prison settled down into the old routine, near-inedible grub served on plastic plates, heavy punishments for minor offences, brutal beatings in the chokey block and the daily monotony which changes

212

men into human vegetables. I talked to some of the cons who remembered the '69 riots, and they told me hair-raising stories of prisoners rampaging through the wings, climbing on to the roofs and tearing off the slates to throw down into the yards, barricading themselves in the television rooms and setting the staff at defiance. One of the blokes who had been in the television room along with some really hard cases, including the notorious 'Mad Frankie' Fraser, gave me a graphic account of what happened when they volunteered to return to the cells. This is what he told me, in his own words as far as I can remember them.

We say we're coming out and open the doors. There's a long tunnel from the TV room to the wings, and it's lined with screws, both sides. They've all got sticks. As we come out a screw shouts 'another one coming'. We go out one by one. They don't touch us, but when they shout a name, like 'Fraser coming' or whoever, they go to work with the sticks. They gave Fraser a right seeing-to, and a few more too. Fraser has more stitches put in him than all the screws put together. The ones who had their names called were nicked as ringleaders. They all had time added on. Frankie got five and the others between three and six'.

It set me to wondering why cons riot. After all, they're on a hiding to nothing. Once the riot has started there's no chance they can get away, all they can do is give in at the end. Looking at it from the prisoner's point of view, which very few people do, they must be in a desperate state to risk further additions to their already long sentences.

I don't wish to fudge the issue. A villain commits a crime and goes down for it, and he doesn't expect to be sent to a convalescent home. On the other hand, having been deprived of that most precious thing, his liberty, he has the right to demand that he gets comparatively decent treatment providing he behaves himself. For example, a con is expecting a visit from his wife and kids and they don't turn up. He worries himself sick wondering what might have happened then, days later, he gets a letter from his wife saying that she phoned the prison explaining why she couldn't come. He makes enquiries. Yes, the message was received but 'what the fucking hell do you think we are, a messenger service?' is the only reply he would get.

Of course they're not a messenger service, but what does it cost for a screw to pass on a message, 'tell so-and-so that his wife isn't coming, she'll write later'. Actually one of the decent screws would do just that. It's the bastard screws who love to dish out the mental torture. At the bottom of it all is the absence of an effective system for considering legitimate grievances. Under the present system the prisoner has no chance, he is a liar and guilty before he opens his mouth. The Governor believes the screw, the Visiting Committee believes the Governor and the Home Office will believe anybody bar the prisoner.

Parkhurst is the home for criminal 'headliners'. Stand on any corner of the exercise yard and you will be passed by some of the most infamous characters in British criminal history.

There were the Hussain brothers, a pair of Asians who kidnapped the wife of a national newspaper executive and held her to ransom. When the money was not forthcoming the lady disappeared, and the brothers were convicted of her murder. I had a long chat one day with the elder brother and, with natural curiosity, tried to find out what had happened to the lady's body, which was never found.

'They almost pulled the farm to pieces looking for

it,' he said, laughing all over his face. 'We wouldn't be so stupid as to bury her on the farm. She's in the last place you would ever think of looking, but it's one place where you could expect to find her.'

This one was a real funny fellow. Whenever I saw him he was running as though he had to get somewhere in a hurry. Even the way he ran was peculiar, a high-stepping trot like one of the performing horses in a circus.

The man christened the Cambridge Rapist by the popular press was a queer fish. I had expected to see some form of super athlete when I first laid eyes on him, but he was an insignificant figure, about five feet six, with long hair below his shoulders. He had a profitable business renting out his court depositions for tobacco when he first arrived. They put the hard porn magazines to shame.

Von Bulow was walking along a road in Caterham when a police car pulled up and a copper stepped out, wanting to know what he had in the bag he was carrying. It turned out to be a Luger pistol, which the suspect promptly emptied into the officer's body, killing him stone dead. The murderer was hunted for four weeks by posses of armed police, much to the disgust of the Surrey villains who were forced to stay indoors at nights due to the activities of the Old Bill. The name von Bulow was assumed, deriving from an ancient German prince, all part of a Teutonic obsession. He used to stroll about constantly clenching and flexing his fingers as though practising a quick draw with a six gun.

There was a small group of inmates who kept themselves very much to themselves. They had been convicted of terrorist activities in Birmingham and London where they were said to have planted a bomb in a pub (Birmingham) and one in the Central Criminal Court

(London). The explosions caused considerable loss of life and injury to innocent members of the public. From my contact with them I found it hard to believe that they could have been guilty of such cowardly crimes. They were just decent Irish blokes who happened to be in the wrong place at the wrong time and suffered for it.

Johnny Brook had been convicted of the murder of Muriel Patience at the Barn Restaurant on Guy Fawkes night 1972. Another man was twice tried and twice acquitted on the same charge. He was George Ince, a former associate of the Kray twins and Dolly Kray's lover. Brook was a loner. He had an artificial right eye which gave him a rather peculiar expresion. This glass eye looked right at you while the other roamed about all over the place.

Danny Allpress and Bryan Turner were two outstanding characters. Danny had been put away by supergrass Bertie Smalls, and kept a budgerigar in his cell which he had taught to say 'Bert is a fucking grass'. Danny and Bryan had pulled off robberies at the Ilford and Wembley branches of Barclays bank amounting to close on four hundred grand gets.

Ex-commando Harry Roberts, who killed three Old Bill in Braybrook Street near Wormwood Scrubs, was one of the hard cases. After the killing, when every copper in the London area was looking for him, he stayed at liberty for a month, hiding out in Epping Forest. Another cop-killer was Fred Sewell, who shot an inspector in Blackpool and was later mixed up in an attempted break-out from Gartree. He told me how one of the screws copped for one of the escapers and repeatedly smashed him over the head with a claw hammer, which sparked off a riot. Then there was Bill Skindle, who also killed a copper by putting nine bullets into him.

Johnny Kellard, serving sixteen years for bank robbery, was captured after a bizarre incident in Kensington High Street, a fashionable London shopping centre. The gang, waving their shooters, were just making a getaway from the bank when, out of the blue, a copper came on the scene. He was just leaving his post at a local embassy and, like all Old Bill on that sort of duty, carried a gun. Proving the point that property, especially bank money, is more valuable than life, the copper sprayed the surrounding scenery with bullets, shot Johnny in the thigh and also wounded another member of the gang by the name of Hart. Johnny was nicked, but Hart managed to make his way to the multi-storey car park where he had left his car. He bled to death beside it.

There were many others serving long sentences either for armed robbery or murder, and all of them, at one time or another, had been in the Special Security Block, known as the SSB. This was a two-storey building about the size of a largeish detached house which had electronic locks, closed circuit television cameras, a wired-in exercise yard and batteries of floodlights. It was considered escape proof, but there were three cons who didn't agree with that. They were bank robbers Johnny Kellard and Cyril Burkett and cop-killer Bill Skindle. One afternoon they broke out of the block, cut through the wire-mesh fence enclosing the exercise yard and were away. They split up, Kellard and Burkett making for the houses and a chance of nicking a car, Skindle for the woods near the prison.

The two bank robbers were captured within the hour, but Skindle, a natural lifer with nothing to lose, had not been found by nightfall. The following morning armed police with an SAS unit were out combing the area, and a helicopter was also brought into the hunt, equipped with a detection device which could pick up a human body from its heat radiation. Poor old Skindle. He didn't have a chance.

As usual, the Home Office over-reacted. They didn't just close the door after the horse had bolted, they nailed it, screwed it, padlocked it and barred it, shoved the horse back through the only window and then bricked that up. Actually the SSB was immediately evacuated and the prisoners shifted under heavy escort to other jails all over the country. Then, working on the principle that the best way of holding up a pair of trousers is belt, braces and six-inch nails in the hips, the brains went to work. First they replaced the perimeter fence with a steel-lined concrete wall, topping it with an overhanging rubber coping incorporating a pressure-pad alarm, then they built a tunnel-proof exercise yard, alarmed all the windows, installed sufficient search-lights to illuminate Piccadilly Circus and finally ringed the area with a dozen television cameras. When this work had been completed the prisoners were brought back to their new hermetically-sealed environment.

One of the old mates I was very glad to see again was John Thorne, who was doing fifteen years for armed robbery. He had a very interesting tale to tell, for he was one of the many who had been sent down on the evidence of a new breed of law enforcer known as the supergrass.

What is a supergrass? He is, quite simply, a criminal who buys immunity for his own crimes by informing on fellow criminals on a mass scale. Maurice O'Mahoney turned Queen's Evidence when John Thorne was charged in connection with the armed robbery of a Securicor van in Heston in 1974. They were on this job together. Four other men were also concerned.

The scene of the robbery was Phoenix Way, Heston,

the date June 1st 1974. The Securicor van was rammed by a low-loader and four men in another van parked nearby leapt out, captured the loot and escaped in a stolen Jag. The following extracts are from statements O'Mahoney made to the Old Bill, which were the basis of the evidence he gave at the trial.

"As I was sitting in the back of the van waiting I had a touch of bottle and said to John Thorne 'what am I doing here, I've got a lovely wife and kids at home' and he said 'if you don't get out of this van I'll blow your fucking head off'. He then pointed the shotgun at my head."

Later in the statement:

"The driver then opened the inside door which leads to the back of the van because Thorne threatened to shoot the guard in the legs and as the guard was getting out I got in and saved the guard from getting shot in the legs because I was in the line of fire. If it wasn't for me that man would have been shot dead."

Further on in the statement this poignant cry from the heart:

"It was too much. Thank God the security man didn't die. I'm going to help the police and tell them a number of other jobs I've been on. I just wish to God I'd never got involved with crime and these sort of animals I've been associating with. I repeat I'm glad it's over, thank God."

Now who was this fellow O'Mahoney who provided the evidence to put away dozens of other criminals? Between 1969 and 1974 he was in on over a hundred jobs, the loot totalling more than two hundred grand in cash and goods. Armed robbery, conspiracy, receiving, house, shop and warehouse breaking, practically every crime in the calendar was committed by this man who suddenly became an upright and model citizen after being nicked and leaned on by the law.

What was his punishment? He was given a five year sentence, spent twenty months in a police cell having it off with his bird when he felt like it (so much for the lovely wife and kids) and going out on parole at the end of the twenty months.He didn't even see the inside of a prison. I for one don't envy him. I'd rather keep my mouth shut and do my bird with a clear conscience. So would John Thorne, who took it all very calmly and merely remarked that the supergrass was just one more hazard in a most risky profession.

For what weight it carries, I'd like to put in my twopennorth, which is biased on the side of the villain. I agree that the law has every right to collect evidence where and how it can, even from supergrasses, but there's something wrong somewhere in this 'cough and all is forgiven' business. When the Old Bill virtually says 'go and nick as much as you like, come and tell us all, throw in plenty of bodies and you can go home', there's the smell of an unholy alliance which doesn't reflect much credit on the dignity and impartiality of the Law.

CHAPTER FOURTEEN

JOE:

Nobody knows what prison is like until they've spent a few years in one. This isn't a very original remark, in fact it's been made many times before, but it's none the less true. There's been a lot of guff written and spoken about prisons, most of it ill-informed rubbish, some of it having the hallmark of Home Office evasion and a little of it true. In the middle seventies there was a lot of press comment about prison conditions, one paper in particular doing a big piece on the treatment of mentally unstable inmates within the system which proved one thing at least. The writer knew almost nothing about prisons, even less about prisoners and nothing at all about the prison system.

This particular ornament to the journalistic profession happily prattled on about 'psychopaths' as though they were some strange breed to be found in prison and nowhere else. I looked up the word in the dictionary where I learned that a psychopath is 'one who shows a pathological degree of congenital emotional instability without organic mental disorder' or, to put it into everyday language, somebody who does peculiar things but isn't an actual nutter. By my reckoning that includes pretty well everybody in the country from the Prime Minister down to the lowest individual in the social scale. It certainly includes the habitual criminal.

I learned a lot about the treatment of the so-called 'nutter' during the time I spent in Rampton, where the only spark of sympathy was shown by the doctor who recommended my release. I received further education in that area when I spent six months in what was known as the nutter's wing in Parkhurst where I met up again with the Kray twins, Ronnie and Reggie. I had known them well on the outside but hadn't seen them for several years. The wing in which they were confined was special in the sense that it never contained more than thirty inmates and the surroundings were very different to the rest of the prison. There was a greater area of space to move around in, the cells were brighter and cleaner, there were showers that could be used at any time, there was a well equipped gymnasium and two television rooms.

The main thing that struck me when I first went on the wing was the atmosphere of calm and contentment. There was none of the usual shouting and bawling that went on in other parts of the prison and the staff appeared to be out of the general run of screws in that they went about their work quietly and unobtrusively, rarely raising their voices and avoiding arguments. All this was unusual but, as I settled down and learned more about what was going on, I realised that somebody somewhere was making an effort to deal with a real problem in a realistic way.

So far in this book I have been critical of the manner in which the authorities deal with that small minority of cons known to them as psychopaths but referred to simply as nutters. These are men who are a danger to themselves, their fellow prisoners and the prison staff. They are normally serving long sentences and their actions are unpredictable. In my experience what generally happens is that the prison regime lumps together the so-called psychopath, the mental defective and the persistent offender under one roof and then uses repressive violence to iron out the creases so to speak.

A situation would arise where a right lunatic would talk out of turn to a hard-case heavy whose speciality was armed robbery, not shitting on a neighbour's rose garden or wagging his willie at the vicar's wife. The heavy would stick one on the loony and the psychopath, ever ready to join in on a bit of GBH, would march in with his contribution. The matter was then settled by the screws who had no alternative but to go in with the big stick, knock the combatants senseless and bang them up in the chokey block. The point I am making is that if these three cons were segregated in different parts of the prison there'd be less need for the heavy mob and a more peaceful atmosphere all round.

Giving credit where credit is due I have to admit that an honest attempt was being made in the nutter's wing to deal with the problem of the uncontrollable con. There was evidence, to my mind, that someone had made a careful study of these men and worked out that segregation and proper medical treatment was more effective than the use of the big stick. The consequence was that some of the hardest and most brutal inmates were controlled by the careful administering of sedatives, a much more civilised method of maintaining order than meeting violence with violence. Cracking skulls does not cure mental disorders. All it does is fill beds in the prison hospital.

I had a good example of the efficacy of this treatment right under my nose. Ronnie Kray, who had a reputation for violence on the outside, was no less violent when it came to a showdown either with the screws or with one or other of his fellow prisoners. Early on in the beginning of his life sentence the authorities had placed him in a separate prison from his twin brother. Ronnie celebrated this event by going on a spree of violence, smashing up the prison canteen for starters and repeating the process when he was released from the chokey block. In the end the authorities re-united him with

Reggie, but there was always the danger that he would go into one on the slightest provocation, and sometimes for no apparent reason. Naturally he had to endure some fairly serious whacking before being subdued, but that didn't seem to make any difference to his behaviour. He soaked it all up and came back for more.

He was the perfect example of of the type of prisoner that I described earlier in this chapter, a danger to himself, to the prison staff and to his fellow inmates. Early on in his criminal career and while serving a short sentence for a crime of violence he had been diagnosed as suffering from schizophrenia which, according to the dictionary, is a condition characterised by progressive deterioration of the personality, withdrawal from reality, hallucinations, delusions, social apathy, emotional instability etc. What the etc stands for I have no idea. Anyway, the enlightened methods of treatment practised in the nutter's wing, while not curing his disorder, at least rendered him tractable. It is a tribute to whoever thought up the idea of treating sick prisoners like human beings and caring for their welfare that Ronnie Kray enjoyed some quality of life.

I spent considerable time in the company of the twins. Having known them back in the sixties, when they were real terrors and either respected or feared by London's mobsters, I was agreeably surprised by the change they had undergone.

They were still classified as security risks and, among the borderline cases on the wing, they kept themselves pretty much to themselves. From time to time some of the inmates would take a liberty which would have been unthinkable when the twins were free men. Ronnie was occasionally subjected to stupid remarks which would have earned a vicious striping on the outside but, using his mouth instead of his fists, he put the idiot to rights and it all ended with muttered apologies.

Under this enlightened regime Ronnie spent his time reading, writing poetry and listening to music, mostly of the classical variety. He also tried his hand at painting and some of his work was surprisingly good according to certain art experts, who likened his canvasses to those of the American primitive, Grandma Moses.

Reggie was a different kettle of fish. Unlike Ronnie, who took little exercise and had put on a considerable amount of weight, his twin was fanatical about fitness. Reggie spent hours in the gym going through a punishing series of exercises, including weight lifting. As a result he was in almost perfect physical condition. His mental approach to the prospect of spending most of his adult life behind bars was difficult to determine. He had always been the quieter one and, though he appeared to have come to terms with prison life, I sensed that there was a memory from the past that troubled him. I came to the conclusion that the one great sadness which he experienced when he lost his wife still remained at the back of his mind. Those who were close to him when the tragedy occured were of a similar opinion.

After a period of six months on the wing I decided that enough was enough, but I found it harder to get out than it had been to get in. I tried every trick in the book and finally wrote to my MP, St. John Stevas, who put my case to Lord Harris at the Home Office with the result that I was moved back to B wing and my old job as a cleaner.

I managed to get a glance at some of the correspondence that passed between the MP and his Lordship on the subject of 107932 Cannon J.D. It was an education in the use of bullshit, fiction and outright fantasy. Running right through the rigmarole was the usual thread of argument which makes out that the con is a simpleton, a trouble maker and a liar all at the same time, while the prison department is made up of reasonable people doing their best to create order out of the chaos that they themselves manufacture

Knowing the true circumstances of life in prison I can't find it in myself to blame cons who riot and take hostages. It's their only way of being heard. Surrounded by secrecy and cover-up, they reach a stage of desperation where drastic action is called for, so they take it. Believe me, it's not just mindless violence. They're up against a repressive system thats been perfected over centuries and secrecy is an essential part of it. Prisons are insulated from the outside world. If the public knew only one-tenth of what goes on inside these places they would join in the riots too, Brutal discipline, lack of adequate medical treatment, denial of access to legal advice, restriction and censorship of letters, once-a-month visits and the petty irritations of ironclad rules and regulations all add up to the creation of situations which are guarantied to explode in violence.

The worst feature of the system comes to the fore towards the end of a sentence. It is then that the con is eligible for release on licence, commonly known as parole, and this is how it works. When a prisoner has done one-third of his time his case comes before the Local Review Committee who decide whether it should go to the Parole Board. Once past that hurdle, the Board considers the prisoner's dossier and reports on his behaviour and then comes to a decision. If parole is turned down, no reason is given and there is no appeal against it. It works out in practice that a prisoner serving, say, twelve years is considered for parole after serving four. If he hasn't been a good boy he gets knocked back. His case then comes up again after a period of time in which he is kept in promise land and may be knocked back again. What can happen, and often does, is that a man can serve his full time but during eight years of it he is kept in a state of nail-biting uncertainty. Beat that for refined torture.

Of course there is every reason to say that the con has committed a crime, he has been given twelve years and he should serve every day of it. Fine and dandy, then abolish the parole system and don't burden a man who has enough on his mind already with vague promises of release. The Parole Board, whose activities are shrouded in secrecy and who are not accountable for their often inexplicable decisions, are above common justice and humanitarian considerations. Like cunning old Fury in 'Alice in Wonderland', they are judge and jury, they try the whole cause and condemn you to a fate worse than death. In my case I served six years of an eight year sentence, but then I wasn't a good boy so I couldn't expect much by way of time off for good behaviour.

Going back to the time when I had a dust-up with the screws at Wandsworth, I had been granted permission, for what it was worth, to consult a solicitor about taking a civil action against the two screws, Mason and Cheyney, who had given me a good kicking. This business had been going on for the best part of five years with the Home Office putting every obstacle in the way, holding up letters, making it difficult for the solicitor to see me on various pretexts and in fact doing everything possible to prevent the case coming to court. As an example, one letter to the Home Office requesting certain details was not answered for twenty-two months!

At the same time as this palaver was going on I had a claim in for some clothing which had gone missing from my property, again at Wandsworth. Admittedly the place was full of thieves, but that was hardly my responsibility. I hadn't put them there. The Home Office started off by denying all responsibility, but finally paid £80 into court, a cunning dodge well known in legal circles which meant that, if I went on with the action, any further costs incurred were down to me. I cut my losses and took the cash. The affair had its humorous side, because I had bought the expensive Crombie overcoat and the other gear out of the proceeds of crime. I also had a giggle when I thought of a battery of lawyers being hired by the Home Office to administer a legal licking to a lowly con.

When the case against the screws finally got to court it was the 3rd November 1977. I was sent up from Parkhurst for the hearing and given temporary accommodation in that penal dustbin (I quote an ex-governor's description) Wormwood Scrubs.

The comic opera opened when I appeared before the court to conduct my own case, clad in prison clothing and carrying a bulging briefcase. Mason and Cheyney were represented by solicitors supplied by the Prison Officers Association and Lord Harris of the Home Office by a Treasury Department legal eagle. Ranged against this small army I prepared to do battle.

It all turned out to be a nonsense. The judge listened for a while to the legal prattle, then put a stop to the proceedings by declaring that the action was out of time. The delaying tactics of the Home Office had arbitrarily decided the outcome without my being able to offer any evidence. The judge gave the legal representatives a mild ticking-off, recorded his disapproval of the way the Home Office had behaved and finished awarding costs against me!! It's a sad reflection on the state of things that, had I been a free man, the matter would have been disposed of in three months at the outside. So much for going through the proper channels. I swore there and then that the next time a screw laid a hand on me I'd punch his fucking head in. I say arseholes to a system that denies common justice to a man because he's a con.

I have to say I was disgusted by the performance of Mason and Cheyney outside the court. As I was led away under escort this pair of animals stuck out their tongues and laughingly gave me the old two-finger salute. It was very fortunate for them that I was cuffed up because, if I'd had my hands free, I would have taught both of them a right lesson.

During the few days I was in London I was shuffled about between the Scrubs and Pentonville. The business of being kept on the move was intended to make it difficult for any of my mates to visit me, thus saving them the long trip to the Isle of Wight. I heard later that quite a few of them had been turned back at the gates, being told by the screws that my whereabouts were not known. All I can say is that it is a bloody queer prison system that doesn't know where its prisoners are. Another thing that got up my nose was that, as I went from one nick to the other, all the papers in connection with my legal business were read over and over again by screws who were only animated by curiosity and not security. By the time I got back to Parkhurst my documents were pretty worn and well finger-marked.

At both the Scrubs and the Ville I met up with old acquaintances. One of them told me of the reception given to ex-Commander Virgo and his confederates who had been sent down in the notorious pornography trials for corruptly accepting bribes. These former pillars of the police force, who were soon transferred to Ford open prison, refused to leave their cells, shit-scared that some of the cons would take it into their heads to even up a few old scores. My own feelings about these fellows is uncompromising. A villain is a villain and makes no secret of the fact, but I have no time for men who masquerade as law enforcers then use their privileged positions to break the laws they are pledged to uphold. Later when, as a free man, I assisted in the Countryman enquiry, I made my feelings quite plain.

Not having been in the Scrubs for some years, I naturally was quite interested to see the changes that had taken place since I was last there. I landed up in a cell with a couple of kids when I came up from Parkhurst, and I was surprised, to say the least, that a hardened villain such as myself should be brought into close association with juveniles. I would have thought that the authorities would have gone to extreme lengths to keep me away from contact with easily-influenced youngsters. One of them, just twent-one years of age, was serving a sentence of four years. He cried himself to sleep every night. The other kid was a bit harder, but then he'd had Borstal and was only in for twelve months, a cake-walk as he proudly told me. I could see he had the makings of a right villain, accepting bird as one of the natural hazards of his chosen trade.

I was even more surprised to see some real hard cases mixed in with the youngsters. There was a bloke called Cheeseman who had done a long stretch in Broadmoor during which time he murdered another inmate, another one by the name of Reed who had robbed and killed a taxi-driver. There was also a chap called Powell, a very hard man indeed, who had done eight months in the chokey at Dartmoor and was now at the Scrubs for re-allocation. To house such men as these under the same roof as a bunch of impressionable kids was asking for trouble and, as I heard subsequently, it was not long in coming. It culminated in the resignation of the Governor, who sent a now-famous letter to the Times stating why he had decided to quit. He's a lone voice crying in the wilderness, but then so was Winston Spencer Churchill once upon a time.

After the heady excitements of the Metropolis and the delights of the Scrubs and the Ville I returned to Parkhurst just before Christmas. My parole was due to come up early in the New Year, and the way I saw it they would be glad to be rid of troublesome 107932 Cannon J.D. Still there was a bit of a way to go, and who knew what was waiting round the corner.

I went back on B wing and my old job as a cleaner. One day the powers that be called for volunteers to clean out the empty cells which were liberally decorated with pigeon shit, dead mice and rats and the odd deposit of human excrement where a con had been caught short. I was approached but turned the job down. However, a couple of blokes did volunteer. They were budgerigar fanciers so I suppose they felt at home in the middle of the heaps of bird shit.

Actually there were quite a number of budgie fanciers at Parkhurst. They kept the bird for company and many a cell door carried a notice DO NOT ENTER, BUDGIE LOOSE. The little things were well-trained and very tame and flew about the wing without making any attempt to have it away, which they could have done quite easily with no fear of being brought before the Governor for trying to break out. There was one inmate who acquired a young bird from a breeder with the intention of making it the tamest, sleekest, fattest, most beautiful and well-spoken bird in the nick. He lashed out on an exotic cage, birdseed, millet, cuttlefish and all the paraphernalia available to the besotted owner of a pampered bird. It died that very night. The following morning the bereaved owner picked up the stiff little body and, holding it in front of his face, gave forth.

'You fucking ungrateful bastard,' he bellowed. 'I

spent a fortune on you and all you could do was fucking snuff it.'

There were many ways in which the men passed their time, apart from keeping budgies. Model making, using matchsticks as material, was one of them. One bloke had made a church about four feet high with pews and altar and all the interior fittings. It was a beauty. There were any number of boats of all shapes and sizes from ancient Spanish galleons to cabin cruisers, all made from odd bits of wood and correct down to the last rope. There were also a few budding Picassos who spent all their money on oil paints and turned out what seemed to be the sort of work that was worthy to be hung in any art gallery.

It sounds incongruous but one of the lifers was an opera singer who often felt the need to let himself go. He would choose a time when the table tennis room wasn't being used and would walk about, his hands behind his back, filling the air with excerpts from various operas in a glorious tenor voice. Even the roughnecks stopped watching television to listen to the performance. Music hath charms...

The more I see of prisons the more I am surprised by some of the remarkable happenings within those grim walls. In Parkhurst there were about four hundred or so inmates living in conditions of almost indescribable squalor, denied normal sexual relationships and working out their frustrations by slaughtering each other or having a go at the screws. Yet when Ron Strutton collapsed and died one morning while he was drinking a cup of tea the whole of the prison rallied round. His daughter was due on a visit that day. She was met at the gate and told that her father was ill and could not be visited and so was saved the misery knowing that she would never see him alive again. The Governor gave permission for a collection to be taken up for Ron's widow, which raised the considerable sum of three hundred pounds, most of which came from the meagre wages of the cons. It all tended to restore one's faith in humanity.

Prison is not without its humorous incidents, though they are few and far between. There was the occasion of a football match which took place when a Parkhurst side met a Sport and Showbiz eleven. The event was reported in the local paper. Quite seriously the sides were given as:

SPORT AND SHOWBIZ SIDE	PARKHURST PRISON SIDE
Tosh Chamberlain	No. 224057
Johnny Evans	265876
Dennis Puttock	756452
Joe Wallis	245098
Barry Francis	768743
George Francis	675698
Roy Francis	875321
Dennis Pinching	987874
Tony Sutton	843125
Joey Singleton	245376
Jimmy Langley	256879

No kidding! The writer lost the chance of an extra bit of comedy. He could have referred to Dennis Pinching's opposite number as Charlie Thieving!

One day a bunch of us were watching television when a programme came on called Day by Day. It was a news and comment affair, not Sir Robin talking about himself. An item was shown about an aircraft race from Southsea to Lydd and, as the entrants were being introduced, the picture switched to an aerial view of

Parkhurst. 'Parkhurst prison,' said the commentator, 'home of England's blackest villains, where tonight the men have bet their last ounce of tobacco on their Deputy Governor winning the race. Then came a picture of the afore-mentioned prune in a Mickey Mouse plane with a Volkswagen engine. The television room echoed to derisive roars and jeers. Next morning, pinned to the notice board and read by almost everybody before it was taken down was the following epic poem.

> On Day by Day the other night
> The viewers all were told
> That we, the blackest villains
> All had hearts of gold.
> We loved our dear old deputy
> And would all scream and shout
> To hear that he had won the race
> We'd backed him with our snout.
> But they had got it slightly wrong
> The snout we'd pay with glee
> To someone who would fix his plane
> To come down in the sea.
> Happy? We would raise the roof
> And cheer quite fit to burst
> To hear the lifeboat got there late
> And the sharks had reached him first

Just the sort of comment that could be expected from England's blackest villains.

On the 8th of May 1978, Jacques Mesrine, the most notorious criminal in France, made a spectacular escape from La Sante prison in Paris. A few hours before he went over the wall, another less well-known malefactor was let out through the gates of HM Prison, Parkhurst, Isle of Wight.

I was out but not really free. As a convict on licence I was under the control of the Home Office probation service, and for the next eight months my movements would be closely supervised. I would have to live an industrious life, keep away from bad company and generally behave myself. If I stepped out of line I stood a good chance of being back in the boob in double quick time,

I had a few drinks on the ferry and took a long luxurious piss in a clean sweet-smelling lavatory for the first time in years. At Portsmouth I boarded a train and in a little over an hour I was at Victoria station.

CHAPTER FIFTEEN

ELLEN:

If somebody says to me that so-and-so is a face I know exactly what is meant. In underworld slang a face is a criminal who is known to his associates and also to the police. In a minority of cases he is also known to the general public due to television and the press. The gang who robbed the mail train in '63 had their pictures plastered all over the pages of the national press and some of them appeared on television. Ronnie Biggs features are as well-known as those of the man next door. Millions of readers of the various books about the Kray twins and the Richardson brothers would recognise them in the street.

My Joe started his apprenticeship as a face at the age of twenty when he became Jack Spot's minder. Jack himself was a face and so were Billy Hill, Albert Dimes, Frankie Fraser and many others. It was curious that women were not referred to as faces but then they didn't carry out armed bank raids and suchlike. I did notice one thing and that was the men who were mixed up with high-level City crime such as the Guiness affair were never called faces. There's a moral in that somewhere.

Naturally I knew most of the faces because some of them were frequent visitors at our home when some blag or other was in the planning stage. I think I can say with absolute truth that I have provided tea and sandwiches for many of the most notorious villains in the country. I often thought that these gatherings must have been rather like board meetings in some City office except the accents were not so polished and the general behaviour was more boisterous. Not that any of our visitors stepped out of line. There was no coarse language, at least not when I was in the room with them, though I'm sure there was plenty of effing and blinding when my back was turned.

To get back to the Dale, Joe had finished his sentence at Blundeston and I must mention here that this was the first time he had gained maximum remission on his sentence for good behaviour. This says something for the enlightened regime in that prison. It's a pity there aren't more jails like it. Understandably Joe steered clear of our home and was off on some mysterious business in North London and all I had from him was a few phone calls to let me know he was in the land of the living. I understood the reason for this. On his home manor he was always liable to be pulled in if a job went off in the area. It was logical to seek fresh fields.

I was certain about two things. Joe would be back home after some time had passed or he would be nicked once more and in prison. Whichever way it turned out I would be waiting to do what had to be done. In the meantime I was quite content, looking after my little Kim who was growing up into a very bonny young lady. Of course I had to cope with the usual questions, where's Dad, when is he coming home, but she seemed satisfied with my answers. So time passed. There were telephone calls and the occasional meeting at some convenient place away from the Dale. Joe appeared to be doing very well for there was plenty of money being put indoors. I didn't ask questions. If Joe wanted me to know what he was up to he would have told me. Since he didn't tell me I presumed it was none of my business.

At that period of my life I don't think I had much to complain about. I had a nice home, a lovely little daughter and there was no shortage of money. I was in the position of many women whose husbands were away for long stretches and I was quite content. Even when the letter came from Brixton prison informing me that Joe was on remand pending trial at the Old Bailey I wasn't particularly upset. As I had so often done before I made up the parcels of goodies and set off for the wilds of South London.

Joe put me in the picture when I saw him. He didn't go into one or anything like that, just mentioned almost casually that he'd been dropped into the mess by some nasty people. He seemed quite cheerful and told me not to worry because the case against him was a weak one and he was sure that he would come out of it alright. I wasn't so confident myself. With Joe's form anything could happen.

I heard the news about the breakout from Brixton on the television news. It was just a brief item and no names were mentioned but I was sure that Joe was mixed up in it. There were later reports which didn't give much more information. That was provided by a released prisoner who called round to see me and filled me in on the details. It appeared that Joe had teamed up with some old mates to create a disturbance in which four men had it away. One of them was Joe. The three others were Chris Wilkins, Ray Pegler and Richie Payne. I expected that there would be fireworks in the near future with four desperate villains on the run and I wasn't far wrong. The next news to reach me was that the four of them had done a bank in Ilford and got away with several thousand quid.

All I could do was sit and wait for further news. Joe sent the odd message to say he was alright but I had a feeling that it wouldn't be long before he was picked up and I was right. The four of them were recaptured and back in Brixton within a few days. Then came the long wait on remand before they were brought to the Old Bailey for trial. Joe was sent down for eight years.

I now had to face up to a big change in my life. At the age of thirty-two I was pregnant. Kim was a baby no longer but a young woman and, when young Jimmy came into the world she was delighted with her tiny brother. Joe had started serving his sentence in Chelmsford and he saw his son for the first time in a prison visiting room.

There wasn't a lot to look forward to in the immediate future. Even with the maximum time off Joe would spend the next six years behind bars. However I did not lack support. I had all I needed from family and friends and Joe, bless him, had made sure that I was not short of money. Added to that I had a nice home so there were compensations which helped to make life more bearable. All in all I wasn't so badly off in the circumstances - there were many worse off than I was.

So time rolled by. Young Jimmy was a good baby and I lavished on him all the care and attention of which I was capable. Joe had been transferred from Chelmsford to Parkhurst on the Isle of Wight which made visiting more of a hassle what with the long train journey from Paddington and the ferry trip over the Solent. He was bearing up well and had met up with some old chums including the Kray twins. I carried out the usual jobs, bearing messages to people on the outside and taking information of the outside world to Joe and his mates.

About this time I began to get concerned about a change that was taking place in the Dale. There had always been a drug problem but it was mainly centred in the All Saints Road area where there was a lot of trafficking in cannabis. To people like the Rastafarians the smoking of marijuana was part and parcel of their religion and the large West Indian section of the population of the Dale did not regard the occasional use of the weed as a crime. It happened almost overnight that the dealers began to handle more dangerous gear. Heroin and cocaine were becoming available in larger and larger quantities and even children were involved. As the mother of a teenage daughter I had to be concerned, though Kim was a very sensible girl who showed no signs of being part of the drug culture in which many of her friends were involved.

I talked about this growing menace to Joe's brothers, who knew pretty well all that went on in the Dale, and they were also disturbed about this new trend. Nobby said that the drug barons had saturated the American market and were now putting a lot of effort and money into opening up outlets in Europe. The name of the Mafia cropped up from time to time as Nobby was convinced that they had the money and the organisation to control this very profitable business. He mentioned certain names of British villains who had gone into the business on the southern coast of Spain and were making fortunes.

On one of my visits I had a quiet word with Joe and told him of my fears. The quiet word was not easy since there was always a screw knocking about within earshot, but we managed it. Joe was worried about Kim which was understandable, but I assured him that I would keep a very close eye on her. I need not have worried. She had a good head on her shoulders. Some of her friends were not so wise. They got hooked on hard drugs, took to mugging and other forms of thieving to pay for them, and the crime rate in the Dale went up by leaps and bounds. This led to increased police activity which didn't please the older villains who didn't approve of the drug scene.

240

There was nothing much happening in London's underworld during the years that Joe was away. Apart from a bit of gang warfare in the West End involving Ronnie Knight and other faces things were pretty peaceful. Joe came home in the spring of '78 to a manor which, apart from the drug pushers, was comparatively quiet. Of course he wasnt completely free as he was on licence, which meant that he had to avoid bad company and report to his probation officer regularly. This didn't worry him too much.

He didn't spend time looking for 'honest work'. A man fresh out of a long stretch isn't exactly the sort of material employers want to take on. Still he wasn't one to let the grass grow under his feet. He went to work for the Blundell brothers, two fellows from Ilford who had made it big in various forms of slightly illegal capers but were respectable to all outward appearances. He did well enough with them to branch out on his own touring the country with his team and selling programmes and souvenirs at the various pop concerts which were all the rage. He made a packet.

Why he decided to give it up and move to Northolt I could not understand. Our daughter Kim had married and was starting a family of her own so we only had Jimmy to worry about, and I suppose that Joe wanted to take the boy away from the Dale and its associations. I had another surprise when Joe came home one evening and told me he had got a job as a cleaner at Heathrow Airport. I couldn't see him in overalls doing dreary manual work and he was not short of money, so why? He joked about it, said it was just a bit of fun and that was all the explanation I received. The balloon went up about three weeks later when one of the Sunday tabloids spread the story of 'The Thief inside Heathrow" across its front page, with a prominent picture of Joe, in overalls and standing beneath the canopy of a cargo shed. According to the reporter who did the story, Joe had got the job without revealing his criminal past, had borrowed(?) the key of the manager's office and taken photographs of the layout of the offices and copied confidential documents. So this was the bit of fun. It didn't strike me that way.

The funny thing is that he wasn't nicked for this caper, maybe because the authorities at Heathrow didn't want to draw attention to the gaps in security which allowed such a thing to happen. From my point of view everything fell into place three years later when a gang of armed men broke into one of the warehouses and captured a haul worth sixty four million pounds, in gold bullion mostly. Was Joe the advance guard? I didn't ask him and he didn't tell me.

CHAPTER SIXTEEN

JOE:

It wasn't a bundle of laughs being on parole as I soon found out. Although the probation officer was no trouble, I had to steer clear of my old mates, who came under the heading of 'bad company'. The usual coming out party did not come off. It would be organised by villains, attended by villains and would be bound to attract the attention of the Old Bill. Also I had to get something that looked like a job of work in order to comply with the 'honest and industrious' life bit which was one of the conditions of my licence.

Within a couple of days of coming out I had a meet with Billy Blundell. He and his brother Eddie were in a big way of business over Ilford way, and they had come a long way since I first met them when they were up at the Old Bailey on various charges in connection with a gun battle outside their mini-cab outfit in Ilford in '71. Eddie was shot in the leg and Billy was severely cut about the face, but they were both nicked and charged with causing an affray.

Eddie had it away but the Old Bill caught up with him in Leicester, and in the end both sides in the battle came up for trial in March of '73: I made a statement for the defence, which was not used, but in the result Eddie and Billy got chucked. We were up at the Bailey at about the same time, and later on both of them paid me a visit at Chelmsford and also came to see me in Parkhurst.

Over the years they had no further trouble with the law. I had postcards from them from all over the place, Tenerife and Torremolinos when they were on holiday, Austria, France, Sweden and Denmark where they toured with the pop group 'Status Quo', and a few letters in which they let me know that I would be looked after when I came out. One postcard I remember particulurly, for Billy had understamped it and I had to pay 22p from my wages before I could read it. 'Hi, Joe having a great time,' it said. 'I'm still working with the Quo, went to a party with the group, plenty of hansom(?) birds. We're in Austria at the moment, might be going to the States. Friend for life, Bill.'

I went out on the town with Billy and, when we parted company in the early hours of the morning, he pressed a wad of notes into my hand and told me to come over to Ilford as soon as possible and he and Eddie would fix me up. Two days later I turned up at their office in Seventh Avenue, Manor Park, and got quite a surprise. They had organised themselves into a very profitable business, selling ice cream and hot dogs to the tourists from vans and trolleys at some of the best pitches in the West End. Eddie explained to me how the system worked. The blokes on the vans and trolleys bought their ice cream cones from him at 70p each, and were given the ice cream itself free. They paid their own expenses, maintained the vans and it was then up to them how much they earned. From some of the stories I had heard about what was known as the 'ice chop', foreigners being charged a couple of quid for a cornet and up to any price for a hot dog, I reckoned that the brothers must be on to at least thirty grand a week in readies in the season, and that was money.

The brothers were a striking pair. Eddie himself was just over six feet and powerfully built and very fit. He didn't smoke and drank very little. At the time he was about thirty eight, but there was nothing middle-aged about his habits. He got up early every morning, went for a swim in the pool at his luxurious house in Mill

Road in Aveley, Essex, and was always at the yard by eight-thirty to get the vans and trolleys on the road. What struck me most about him was his determination. If he wanted something he just went all out to get it, and didn't allow anybody or anything to get in his way.

Billy was a different proposition to his brother, being shorter and lighter and with a tendency to put on weight, but he was a hell of a battler. I think he had more bottle than any man I've ever met, and he certainly didn't know the meaning of the word fear. I got on very well with him, he was much more approachable than Eddie who had a way of keeping people at a distance.

After putting me wise to the 'ice chop' side of his business Eddie gave me an outline of the rest of his business empire. He owned lot of property in the Ilford and Manor Park areas and was into the pop scene in a big way, selling souvenirs and T-shirts at all the big festivals, not only in Britain but on the continent as well.

'We need good men, Joe,' he said. 'If you want to come in, there's a place for you.'

I pointed out that I was on licence and had to be a bit careful about getting into trouble, but he laughed that one off.

'We're respectable business men,' he said, with a wink at Billy. 'You might have to give somebody a slap now and then but that can happen anywhere. We handle a lot of cash. You would·be a sort of security man. It's all the fashion these days.'

I had to laugh at that one. Even Eddie had a smile behind his beard. He changed frequently from being bearded to a close-shaven appearance, a dodge to make positive identification difficult.

'What about my probation officer,' I said. 'I'll have to give her some sort of story.'

'No sweat, I've got a legit property company. You'll come in as a manager.'

That was how I came to go to work for the Blundells. There were a lot of doors closed to an ex-con fresh from Parkhurst, the bullshit about a man having paid his debt to society didn't cut much ice with prospective employers. I won't say I was forced to take on the job, in fact I rather looked forward to it because it was right up my street and the money was very good. In any case, as I saw it, I wasn't mixed up in any criminal business. Eddie and Billy had to protect their interests and they adopted their own measures to do so. When it comes to looking after cash in transit I don't see any difference between Joe Cannon and Securicor, except that I didn't wear a crash helmet, swing a baton or travel in an armoured van.

I fitted into the organisation quite well, and one of the first things I noticed was the loyalty the brothers were able to command among their workers. The only other time I had witnessed that kind of loyalty being shown was when Ronnie and Reggie Kray were at the top of the tree in the sixties. Not that there was any real comparison between the twins and the Blundells. Eddie and Billy were dead clever and, apart from the mini-cab trouble in '71, they had kept clear of the law. I guessed that the local Old Bill was well straightened, because Eddie got away with some diabolical liberties on his own manor.

The brothers had come up the hard way. They came from the Paddington manor in the first place. I believe their old man worked at the same dairy in St. John's Wood that I blagged all those years ago. Their mother was Spanish, and one of their most trusted men was a relative called Jose Larios, known to everybody as 'Pepe'. He wasn't all that to look at, a thin wiry bloke with a Zapata moustache who spent a lot of his time pulling the birds, but he was a wily sort and up to all the strokes. I heard that what was called the 'mini-cab war' was down to him, because he had stepped out of line with a bird from the other mob and started off a chain of events that led to the Old Bailey .

I've come across some colourful characters in my time, but Eddie took the biscuit. He was big in every sense of the word. In the restaurants he frequented he would march in, sit down and expect the staff to give him their complete attention. His car was equipped with a police-type siren which he would switch on whenever he encountered a traffic jam. Then he would tear along on the wrong side of the road, ignoring traffic signals and scattering pedestrians. One time he was going from Manor Park to the West End and a copper on duty at a crossroad waved us on against the red lights. One morning I arrived at the yard to find everything in a turmoil. Some thieving sod had nicked Eddie's siren and he was doing his nut.

There was one incident which almost led to a nicking. Eddie had his own van which he took out occasionally to do the rounds, and he was near Madame Tussaud's when there was a stabbing incident involving an ice cream seller. The first we knew about it was when we were sitting down to lunch in one of Eddie's favourite restaurants, an Italian joint in a side street behind Marble Arch. His van was parked up on the pavement outside and we were just taking our first forkfulls of spaghetti when the Old Bill turned up in force We copped for a right going-over and the van was searched thoroughly but luckily nothing was found to tie us in with the stabbing. I was lucky, because if I'd been nicked I would have been back inside double-quick. Actually the stabbing wasn't down to us but was the result of a personal grudge between a couple of merchants who had no connection with the Blundells.

I was in the office one morning having a chat with Eddie when a phone call came through from one of the workers who operated from a stall outside Tower Hill station. This was one of the most profitable sites in the Blundell set-up. From what I could gather as I listened to the conversation, some comedian by the name of Dave Stubble had fly-pitched his ice cream van next to the stall and started selling.

'Tell him I said to fuck off,' said Eddie.

'I've told him, but he won't go,' said the plaintive voice at the other end. 'He says he's got as much right here as what I have.'

Eddie slammed the phone down.

'Come on, Joey' he said. 'We'll sort this little lot out.'

We shot off in the car and were at Tower Hill within minutes. As we walked towards the station entrance I saw no sign of Dave Stubble, who had got the message and made himself scarce, but some other merchant had nipped in with a load of rubbishy souvenirs. I recognised him as a member of a little firm from North London.

Eddie didn't waste any words but just walked up to this geezer.

'You,' he said 'Fuck off.'

The idiot started to argue.

'I've got as much right here as anybody,' he said.

'No you haven't,' said Eddie.

'Who says so,' said the idiot.

'I say so,' said Eddie. 'Now pack up and fuck off.'

The idiot must have fancied himself as Jack the Lad. He had certainly recognised Eddie, so he should have known better than to turn his back on us, which was a very silly thing to do. I grabbed his shoulder, whirled him round and hit him on the chin. He went down like a sack of potatoes and stayed on the deck.

I said, 'Do you want some more?'

He shook his head. I took a couple of steps forward and kicked his stall up in the air. Eddie and I walked back to the car and scarpered.

These minor incidents of violence were not frequent. It wasn't really necessary to go about hitting people on the chin. Generally the mention of Eddie's name was enough to scare off anybody who wanted to set up in competition. There were the odd cases who were silly enough to argue, then Pepe was told to discourage them. A stink-bomb thrown into the van, a dollop of engine oil in the ice cream or a knife thrust into the tyres of a van were usually sufficient and there were no persistent offenders.

I could see the logic of the brothers' actions. They had a very large stake at risk and the elimination of the competition couldn't be achieved by price-cutting owing to the nature of the business. It was the one on the spot in the fly-pitching game who did the trade and made the money. Since fly-pitching was against the law it was a case of dog eat dog, and the dog with the biggest bark, and of course teeth to match, got the bone.

When I joined them, the Blundells were already into the pop scene. The venues at Wembley, Earl's Court and the Hammersmith Odeon and the open-air festivals at Reading, Knebworth and Blackbush attracted tens of thousands of pop fans. Inside the halls, or the enclosure in the case of outdoor events, the sale of souvenirs, refreshments and so on were in the hands of concession-aires, who paid the promoter a fee, but outside it was a free-for-all. Eddie and Billy, who saw no reason why they should pay for something when they could get it for nothing, were on the outside. The conditions here were different to the ice cream and hot dog trade because there were some right villains attracted by the quick and easy money to be made and that's where the trouble began. The brothers were no pushover, and in the struggle for the best pitches somebody had to get hurt. Eddie and Billy made sure it wasn't them or their workers who suffered.

When the Blundell workers set off for a concert they carried the usual gear for sale, pirated programmes, T-shirts, badges and souvenirs. They also carried Irish Tony, Kevin and Martin whose job was to protect them and keep the opposition in its place. When the firm moved onto a pitch, Irish Tony and his mates made sure that nobody tried to hustle them off. If the pitch they wanted was occupied, then the same trio got rid of the occupant by standing around, hustling him and doing all they could to stop him from trading. It didn't take much of this treatment to discourage the geezer.

Sometimes more drastic measures would have to be adopted. If the opposition was really heavy there was a trio of blacks on hand led by a vicious character known as 'Cowboy'. They wore denims and the kind of stripey woollen hats worn by so many black pop fans. They would worm their way through the crowd, out would come the knives and the victim would be left bleeding on the ground while his attackers melted into the hordes around them. It would all be over in seconds, and eye witnesses could only describe the assailants as 'three black fellows in stripey hats' which gave the Old Bill a choice of a thousand suspects.

Sometimes we had trouble with mobs from out of town. At one concert at the Hammersmith Odeon a firm came down from the North, headed by a villain known as Manchester Freddie. They didn't have much of an organisation and even less gear, but they began to pitch in spite of being warned off and were in a fair way to spoiling our evening. I was in on this concert and took care of Manchester Freddie personally. He went back via the casualty ward of a near-by hospital, very much a sadder and wiser man.

From time to time we had disagreements with concessionaires who had paid for their pitches inside the building or enclosure and didn't like the way we sold our pirated programmes to the fans. When the Electric Light Orchestra gave a concert at Wembley the chap in charge of concessions by the name of Paul Pike thought he would have a go at gobbling us up. He came out of the main entrance to the stadium waving six sets of arms and began to harangue our workers. Apart from being a nuisance he was also wasting valuable time, since concerts do not last forever and lost business cannot be recouped, so Billy, Irish Tony and myself took a hand in the game.

It turned out that Pike was not happy about the quality of our programmes which, according to him, were pirated and in breach of copyright, which they definitely were. Still, as both Billy and I pointed out, this was hardly the time and place to discuss the laws of copyright. Irish Tony said not a word, but he was there. So were we, and we intended to stay. In the end, although all the while our workers had been grafting, we agreed not to sell any more programmes but stood fast on the right to sell the other gear. By this time all the fans were inside so we wouldn't be able to sell any more programmes in any case.

After having been made aware of the facts of life, our friend Mr. Pike was as good as gold, and we had no further aggro with him at Wembley or anywhere else for that matter.

We had one rather funny experience on the Continent. One of the groups, I think it was Status Quo, was appearing in Rotterdam, so a party of workers was sent over with the usual merchandise. Eddie and Pepe were busy at the time, Billy and I were setting up for the David Bowie concert at Earl's Court, so Billy's son, young Billy, was put in charge of the party. On the morning before the show young Billy rang through to tell us that he was having bother with a local firm who had put the block on.

It was typical of Billy that, instead of telling young Billy to pull out, he got on the boat with Kevin and me and we got to the venue just before the concert was due to start. The Dutch firm was operating while our lot stood watching. The three of us walked over to the geezer who seemed to be in charge and, without beating about the bush, Billy let him know that he was putting his workers in. The fellow understood enough English to realise what Billy was saying, and knew enough to tell Billy to fuck off back to England. Billy hooked him one and the fight was on. I put a couple of them on the deck, Billy accounted for two more and Kevin took the tally up to six. After that the Dutch mob gave up and our team moved in.

The funny part was when the guv'nor of the Dutch mob came to Billy on his own to work out some sort of arrangement to get rid of his gear so that the evening wouldn't be a dead loss for him, Billy took the Dutch equivalent of four hundred quid from the fellow in return for which he was allowed to go to work but at quite a distance from the busy main entrance. We did a bomb and the natives didn't do too badly either so far as I could see. We stayed overnight in Rotterdam and did a bit of sightseeing and shopping the following morning. Billy's eye was caught by a beautiful pair of flick knives in one of the shops, which he promptly bought, presenting me with one of them. I stowed it away with the mental reservation that it would only be used for cutting bread. I had finished with guns for ever, and I had no intention of going in for the knife stuff at my time of life.

We got back to London in good time to set up for the David Bowie concert at Earl's Court. There was no trouble and everything was ticking over like a brand new Roller as I stood with Billy at the entrance to the Underground station where we could keep an eye on what was going on. Suddenly I spotted the Dutch firm, mob-handed, coming towards us.

'Heads up, Billy,' I said. 'Here comes trouble.'

The guv'nor of the team came up to us, grinning all over his boat-race and sticking out his hand.

'You give us four hundred pound, we let you work here,'he said.

He was laughing fit to bust at what he thought was a great joke. Billy and I laughed too, but with relief, because they out-numbered us four to one and the situation could have been dodgy. They went in to see the show and afterwards we had a good drink together, a sort of Common Market celebration I suppose you could call it.

By the time I had been with the Blundells for several months I had sussed out the arithmetic of merchandising at the pop concerts. It was a better than double your money proposition. Laying out ten grand brought you back anything between twenty-two and twenty-four, all expenses paid. I thought I would have some of that, so I counted my pennies, found a backer for the remainder and then went to see Eddie and Billy to tell them what I had in mind. They were very good about it, and Eddie even offered to loan me a few grand to get started, an offer which I refused with thanks.

I went in big at the three-day festival at Reading with a good team of workers and minders. I had bought a coach to transport them and the gear. As we were setting up I saw Billy giving us the once-over. His eyes nearly popped out of his head when he saw the size of my operation. I think he was under the impression that I was going into business with a manky little stall in some out-of-the-way corner. That wasn't my idea at all. To cut a long story short, I made a killing and finished up with a good few grand.

I did even better at Blackbush. I had acquired a snide pass with which I got my coach and workers into the enclosure reserved for concession holders. When the balloon went up, which it did very shortly, the security sorted me out and told me in no uncertain terms to pack up and get out. I asked them one simple question.

'Who's going to put me out?' I said.

They took a look at my minders, who were standing about with big grins on their faces, and had a change of heart or, to put another way, a sudden loss of bottle. To start off the proceedings with a battle would have done them no good at all, as they well knew, so we stayed. I had managed to wangle Pepe in with his ice cream van, for which he was duly grateful, so he owed me. I came out of that lot well in front.

I did a few more concerts, but it wasn't all jam and I had plenty of headaches one way and another. It was quite a strain on the nerves, dashing about the country, dealing with suppliers of merchandise, keeping my team together and all that. True, the rewards were fine and more than made up for the inconveniences, but the day came when I decided I had had enough. I disbanded the team, sold off the stock and the coach, paid my debts and called it a day.

254

As for Billy and Eddie, they ran into a lot of trouble. It started as so many of these things do, with publicity in the popular press. In May of '78 the Sun newspaper had a go at Eddie after one of its reporters had got a job on the team and sussed out the operation. Eddie was referred to as the 'Cornet King' and the article contained some very sensational stuff about the strong-arm tactics he used to scare off the competition. Then, in July of the following year, the Daily Mirror had its turn. 'THE CORNETTO MOB GO TO WAR' was the headline, and there were lurid tales of Blundell heavies knocking hell out of the opposition as they captured the cream of the tourist trade outside Harrod's, Madame Tussaud's, the Victoria and Albert and other museums, the Tower of London, Westminster Abbey and various sites in and around Hyde Park.

Curiously enough there wasn't much mention of the brothers' activities in other directions, such as the pop concert scene, but that came later after the Old Bill had taken a hand in the game. According to reports, a number of traders got together and complained to the law that they were being intimidated by the Blundells. Now these traders themselves were law-breakers, flaunting traffic regulations when they fly-pitchcd their vans and often causing considerable obstruction. The Old Bill didn't tell them to piss off. Instead, a special squad of thirty detectives led by two DIs by the names of Lewis and Tucker, set out from Paddington nick on the 29th of October 1980 and rounded up Eddie, Billy, Pepe and a half-dozen others.

The whole story came out when they appeared at the Old Bailey twelve months later on various charges of conspiracy involving blackmail, criminal damage and assault. The prosecution had built up a perfect case, which wasn't surprising considering that they had had over a year to do it in, and a troop of witnesses filed in and out of the box to tell the jury how they had been variously assaulted, had stink-bombs thrown into their vans, their tyres slashed, engine oil thrown into their ice cream containers and so on. The trial started on Tuesday the 10th of November 1981 and ended on Wednesday the 23rd of December. Eddie, Pepe and Roy Chandler, one of the heavies, were all found guilty and by way of wishing them a Merry Christmas, the judge dished out the porridge in what he considered the correct proportions. Eddie got four years and a fine of £2,000, Pepe four years and a fine of £1,000 and Roy Chandler copped for three years. Justice was done; but was it seen to be done?

The Old Bill's point of view was definite. Said one senior detective, speaking of Eddie, 'he is the nastiest piece of work to hit London since the Kray Brothers'. And another: 'It was a classic example of how a ruthless, professional criminal could, by persistent extortion and the use of relatively minor overt acts of violence, gain substantial profit by placing people in fear.' During the six-week trial all sorts of evidence were produced which seemed to me to have nothing to do with the charges. For example, Eddie was said to have a claim against him by the Inland Revenue for nearly two million quid. Everybody knows that an Inland Revenue assessment bears no relation to the amount actually owing. Also it was said that Eddie was negotiating to buy a house at Cranbourne for a quarter of a million. What these facts had to do with bopping some Italian ice cream vendor escapes me, but from the prosecution's point of view it's lovely stuff for arousing prejudice among the members of the jury. I know. I've had some of it.

As an ex-villain I have a fair working knowledge of

criminal law. When this senior detective referred to 'minor overt acts of violence', that's actually quite true, and the sentences for these offences are normally very light; but when conspiracy is added to such charges then the situation changes. Put it this way. If I hit somebody on the chin I would be charged with assault, dealt with in a lower court and probably be fined or, at worst, get three months. If, however, it can be shown that I did this in company with another person, then up comes a charge of conspiracy, it's a job for the Sessions or the Central Criminal Court and the sentence can be very heavy indeed. This was the flanker they worked on the Blundell firm.

Another aspect of the trial was the spectacle of the law taking sides in a disagreement between two gangs of lawbreakers. This sort of action has been the subject of criticism by many eminent jurists. What it boiled down to was that the Old Bill guaranteed immunity to one lot if they would give evidence against the other lot, so there was a very expensive trial, the lawyers paid their fat fees into the bank and Eddie, Pepe and Roy Chandler were removed from circulation for the time being.

So the tourists were protected - or were they? Last summer I watched one of the Eyeties grafting in Exhibition Road, near the museums. He was ripping off the customers to the tune of a couple of quid per ice cream cornet. I took my place in the queue and arrived at the counter of his van.

'Cornet, please,' I said. I tendered a fiver.

He handed me the cornet and three pounds in change.

'Bit heavy isn't it, mate,' I said. 'Where's your price list?'

He gave me a big smile and another pound. Sorry. A little mistake,' he said. 'Next, please.'

Come the summer of 1980, Ellen and I had retired to our country seat. It wasn't a Georgian mansion set in rolling pastures, merely a flat on a council estate in Northolt, but it was a welcome change from Notting Dale where, as a known face, I was always under threat of getting my collar felt for something I hadn t done. I had a good few quid tucked away so we didn t go short, but I wasn't content just to sit around and let it dribble away so I looked about for some sort of straight job which would at least pay for the rent and the groceries.

I heard a whisper that there were jobs going at Heathrow with one of the maintenance sub-contractors there so I went along and applied. They asked me a few questions and when it came to the criminal record bit I didn t actually say no, but shook my head, which was good enough for them and quietened my conscience. Anyway I got the job, which was shift work in the cargo terminal, and started almost immediately.

The cargo terminal was a fascinating place, a massive complex handling hundreds of millions worth of goods every year, a big money box which had been cracked a few times and no wonder, because so far as I could see security was a joke. I was issued with a pass with photograph which had to be worn on the left breast of my overalls at all times, and that gave me the run of the whole place. On the terminal there was a special vault for gold bullion, but I only saw the outside of that.

Of course I was just on borrowed time as I well realised. Sooner or later somebody would put the finger on me, because the Old Bill was forever dodging about. I suppose it was a mixture of curiosity and mischief that led me to conduct the Cannon test on security. What I did was to get hold of the key to the traffic manager's office and have a copy made. Then I took copies over a period of a few days of documentation relating to goods consignments, made a detailed plan of the lay-out of the cargo centre and rounded off the performance by photographing the interior of the offices. There was no criminal intent in this. I merely wondered if it could be done, went ahead and did it, and that was that.

I had been working at the airport about three weeks when the chopper fell. Curiously enough it wasn't wielded by the Old Bill but by a reporter from one of the Sundays who had been tipped off that there was an identifiable villain employed in a vulnerable area at Heathrow. I must say he had done his homework. When he confronted me he was able to tell me as much about my past as I knew myself. He was a very decent sort and really he was only doing his job, so I made a clean breast of everything. Naturally he followed up the story, as a result of which I was fired on the spot. I wasn't particularly worried about this, because I knew it had to happen.

I imagined that the story would rates a few paragraphs in an obscure part of this Sunday paper. To my surprise I was spread all over the front page. I don't think this was because of my pretty face but more because of the enormous gaps in security which the reporter discovered when he followed up his original enquiries. One of the blokes he interviewed was quoted as saying 'you could drive a tank in here and no-one would stop you'. This was fairly strong stuff but a little far-fetched. A tank would be an expensive tool to use on a break-in but who knows? One day an enterprising bunch of villains might make use of one to capture the reward lying in the bullion vaults.

I learned two valuable lessons from this experience. One was that it was pretty hopeless lying myself into a job since my past was bound to catch up with me. The other was that I learned something about the workings of the media which was to come in useful later on when I was to become involved with the press, radio and television on various aspects of crime. Come to think of it, the whole business of reporting crime is a bundle of contradictions. On the one hand the public is quite rightly concerned and wants information about cops and robbers and the tricks they get up to, and there is no doubt that this sort of material sells newspapers and gets high ratings on TV. On the other hand, the Press Council goes all pompous and lays down the rule that ex-criminals should not be permitted to profit from their past activities. Well, I can tell the Press Council this, that no way am I a charitable institution passing information to the media out of the goodness of my heart. I've served a long apprenticeship and paid very dearly for the knowledge I possess and, like any other tradesman, I don't put my talents on the market for free.

The truth of the matter is that both the Old Bill and the Home Office have a vested interest in concealing the truth about levels of crime and prison conditions from the public. The only real information comes from villains, men who really know the inside story, and everything possible is done by the authorities to discredit what they have to say and to put obstacles in the way of their obtaining even elementary justice. As I write these words I have before me the latest statistics. They tell of 45,000 prisoners in jails built for a maximum of 32,000, of men being locked up 23 hours a day, of a huge rise in offences against prison discipline (62,800 in 1981) and of one particular prison, Brixton, where 320 men share four lavatories!

These statistics also record that prison staffs number 23,000, a ratio of roughly one staff to two prisoners and that it costs almost £500 million a year to keep miscreants locked away from contact with 'decent' society. If it wasn't so tragic it would be a bloody joke. Talking about jokes, I saw the Home Secretary on a television programme the other day. Waffling Willie was answering questions put to him by a trio of very on-the-ball journalists and believe me it was a pitiable spectacle to see this unfortunate-looking fellow ducking and diving and dodging the issue. I remember one occasion in Parkhurst when a few of us were watching television. Waffling Willie suddenly appeared on the screen, and the usual chorus of boos went up. One witty bloke remarked that he had a face like a worn-out dishrag, to which somebody replied that the poor fellow couldn't help his looks.

'That's true,' replied the wit, 'but at least he could stay off the telly.'

All this brings me to a point where, as they say in the business world, I have to make a declaration of my interest. Now I've never had much time for politicians. To my mind they are a collection of self-seeking egomaniacs who surface at elections, make a lot of promises which they have no intention of keeping and then disappear into that exclusive club known as the House of Commons where, according to wide-spread reports, they spend most of their time pissing it up and using their privileged positions to promote their private interests. In the past four years the party in power has managed to bugger up the economy, create a huge army of unemployed, remain unmoved as the underprivileged riot in the streets and make no secret of their intention to make the rich richer and the poor poorer. It doesn't make all that difference to me, because I'm a survivor, but I've only one thing to say to the idiots who gave a majority in Parliament to this lot. You deserve all you get. Not that I believe another lot could do better, only that they would have to try very hard to do worse.

To put it in a nutshell I make no bones about describing myself as a male chauvinist. In my opinion women have a place in society, but it doesn't extend to running a country as though it was a grocer's shop in a Grantham back street. I have nothing but contempt for the intellectual bankrupts who bolster the so-called Iron Lady's belief that she is some sort of saviour of mankind, because some of my mates are among the forty-five thousand who would say bollocks to that, and their voices will one day be heard along with the millions who have been thrown on the scrap-heap and denied the chance of earning an honest living. The revolt, dear lady, will start in the prisons, and the big stick you used in the Falklands won't be of much use to you then.

Getting back to my little nest in Northolt, I had come to the conclusion that hunting for a job was a negative occupation, so I put a bit of my capital into a little business where I was answerable to nobody but myself, and if I got the sack it was down to me. However, the past has a habit of bobbing up at the most unexpected times, and that was what happened on the 26th February 1982. Ellen came into the flat from doing her shopping and found a note on the doormat. It was from a Detective Chief Inspector Rattray and it said tersely that he would like to see me and gave a number at which I should ring him to make an appointment. Naturally Ellen was worried sick and tried to get in touch with Rattray to find out what it was all about, but it wasn't until three o'clock in the afternoon that she spoke to him, by which time, as can be imagined, she was doing her nut. It was arranged that Rattray should call on the Monday, which was the 1st of March.

It all looked as though I was going to be fitted up for something, but the Old Bill wasn't going to have it all their own way if I could do anything about it. I set up a tape recorder with a concealed microphone and, when the knock came on the door, I switched it on.

The DCI was accompanied by a Detective Sergeant called Matterson, and they were both very friendly. Ellen made us a cup of tea and we sat down to talk. The first thing Rattray said was that there was nothing to worry about, so I began to worry. It wasn't the first time I had seen the smile on the face of the tiger, and this particular tiger was a very big one. Anybody who makes DCI in the Met has all his chairs at home, but I was reassured by the knowledge that the tape recorder was doing its stuff. If they were going to fit me up I had no intention of going down without a fight.

It turned out that Rattray was from CIB 2, the internal investigation department of the Met, what the Old Bill in conversation between themselves called the 'Rubber Heels', and what he was on about was the three grand that went missing from Valerie Cable's flat when Chris Wilkins, 'Honeypuff' Payne and myself were nicked for the Ilford bank job. Somebody must have had a long memory, because that was ten years back. I put on a 'don't remember' act, which seemed to please Rattray. He then went on to say that he had interviewed Chris, Payne and Ray Pegler, who had told him that the allegations were 'a load of old rubbish'.

There was a lot more of the question and answer, but it was obvious that the DCI didn't really want any information, all he wanted to do was to lose it. He knew that the three grand had been nicked by the law, he knew that I knew the same thing but the object of the exercise was very clear. Wherever the money had gone, it was down to Mr. Nobody. When Rattray saw that I was in two minds about making direct accusations, he came in with the heavy stuff, like I would have to make a statement, be cautioned and give evidence at any resulting inquiry. The last thing I wanted was to be mixed up in an investigation of that kind, which was an invitation to be fitted up, so I took the easy way out and signed a short statement saying that I had no knowledge of any money having been kept by the police.

Rattray seemed quite happy with the outcome and, after having thanked Ellen for the tea and apologised for worrying her, he took himself off saying that he wouldn't need to see me again.

Naturally we both knew that my statement was pure bullshit, but so far as he was concerned it tidied everything up and put a stop to any further investigation. The dossier would be marked 'Case Closed' and disappear into the archives at Scotland Yard, along with many others.

I had a transcription made of the tape recording and read it through very carefully. Whatever other purpose it might serve, I was sure that I was now protected against any backlash. As it happened, the transcript did come in useful later on, when a couple of journalists on the Observer interviewed me in the course of their investigations into police corruption. This led to an exclusive article in that paper on the 25th of April and a few red faces at Scotland Yard when a copy of the tape was handed over to them.

In my opinion it's about time that this business of corruption among the police was put into its proper perspective. After four years and at a cost of four million pounds, Operation Countryman was wrapped up in an atmosphere of slanging matches with the top brass at Scotland Yard, which is not to be wondered at considering the fact that Countryman had named four Commanders, four Chief Superintendents, eight Superintendents, fifteen Chief Inspectors and six Inspectors as being bent. I had followed all the reports in the press very closely, having a personal interest so to speak, because I had done my share of bunging and I waited for the names to turn up. They didn't, Countryman fizzled out and the whole business passed into the hands of Scotland Yard's own investigation department, CIB 2, which explains why Rattray turned up on my doorstep to look into a ten-year-old incident.

Villains are all kinds of things but they're not children, and nobody but a child would be taken in by the Willie Whitelaw waffle about the probity and integrity of the Met. The crime rate is high because villains know they can either get away with it or bribe their way out of it, and the percentage of crime solved is low largely for the same reason. What is more, this evil cannot be stamped out, because the honest cop will protect his bent colleague out of a sense of loyalty, the bent cops close ranks when one of them is threatened and in all this the villain, who is the only person whose evidence can break the racket, sees that evidence discounted because he is held to be working off a grudge or is a natural-born liar anyway.

The most appalling aspect of the situation is the acceptance of this menace by the very top brass at the Yard. Only an idiot would believe that they are unaware of the canker of corruption. Indeed Sir Robert Mark admitted it and tried to do something about it, but he was on a losing wicket and he didn't last long in any case. After him came a pudding-faced Scot, jeeringly nicknamed the 'hammer of Strathclyde', and for all the good he did he might as well have stayed in Glasgow. Now the Commissioner of Police for the Metropolis is a tiny chap with big ideas about quelling riots with plastic bullets but seemingly without a clue as to how to put his house in order. Immoderate language is it? Well, some of us have to stand up and be counted, and I would like to go on record as saying that you can't build a decent, law-abiding society by creating an army of unemployed, encouraging them to commit crime out of desperation, then employing a highly-paid but suspect legal machine to throw them into jail.

Certainly poverty and want are not the sole breeding grounds of crime, but remove from the prisons those who have gone thieving because they're broke and out of a job and the problem of overcrowding is solved. It doesn't make the misery endured in these insanitary shit-heaps any more bearable, but there are fewer to share it. Ian Dunbar, who took over as Governor of the Scrubs from John McCarthy, was quoted as saying 'I have to make certain to have the quality of misery spread over the whole establishment'. What a bloody admission! And what kind of a man would make such a statement? Well, his name will go down in prison history as the Wakefield Governor who ordered the construction of cell accommodation for TWO - yes, TWO - dangerous prisoners. Five cells have been knocked together to provide a room for each man with lavatory, shower and wash basin en suite and a central area with angled glass to allow both to watch a common television set!!

There is more to come. This accommodation will be known officially as D suite, and the front-runners for these desirable residences are Robert Mawdsley, who murdered one fellow prisoner at Broadmoor and two at Wakefield, and David Lant, who was also concerned in the Broadmoor murder. TWO MEN OUT OF MORE THAN FORTY FIVE THOUSAND! I wonder how many cons will be lining up to slaughter each other for the privelege of enjoying similar treatment? And what awaits a con who murders a Governor? The mind boggles at this supreme example of official idiocy.

Descending from cloud-cuckoo land into the real world of prison life, I have news for Willie Whitelaw. If something is not done very quickly to ease the intolerable conditions in the jails of this country he will have a series of riots on his hands the like of which have never been experienced before. The prisons in this country are a disgrace to a civilised society, ancient decaying buildings with primitive sanitation crammed with desperate men, many of whom are locked up three to a cell for twenty-three hours out of the twenty-four. These men have lost their liberty and been robbed of their dignity, they are treated like animals and one day they will react like animals, for they have little to lose.

During my various spells behind bars I've been on pretty close terms with some remarkable people. One of them was a fellow called John Banks who had been mixed up in recruiting mercenaries for the war in Angola. The stories he told were almost incredible, straight out of the Le Carre-Deighton cloak and dagger fiction school, assassination and invasion plots naming ambassadors, diplomats and presidents, huge sums of money changing hands and all that paraphernalia. I actually knew about one of his capers, which had come in for a lot of press coverage and earned him a couple of years, during which he had it away from Coldingley open prison.

One morning in early January '83 this character phoned me to arrange a meet. I was curious to find out what he was after so I turned up with an open mind, ready to listen to whatever proposition he wanted to put up. It turned out that, according to him, he had been approached by certain elements connected with the Togo governments to foil a suspected attempt on the life of their President, a chap called Eyedema. What he proposed was that I should go with him to meet the Togo ambassador in Brussels to discuss what could be done. He made it quite clear that there would be a lot of money in it.

This sort of thing wasn't really my scene but I decided to play along with him for the time being. I had no intention of going in blind, however, so I told him I would let him have an answer the next day and we parted company. I lost no time in shooting round to the public library and filling myself in on all the information I could rake up about the background to Banks' story.

What I discovered was that the Togolese Republic was a small state in West Africa bordering on Ghana with a population of around two-and-a-half million. There was a long history of trouble. President Sylvano Olympio had been assassinated in 1963 and this chap Eyedema, an Army type, had taken over as President in 1967. Olympio's two sons fled the country and set up an opposition in exile, and several attempts had been made to kill Eyedema, the most recent in October 1977. It looked as though Banks was on to something, but I wasn't sure where I fitted into the picture. Anyway I decided to give it a go and arranged to meet Banks at Heathrow at 1.30 pm on the 13th January which was a Thursday and not a Friday. I proved my usefulness right away by paying for two return flights to Brussels, which Banks said would be refunded by the Ambassador.

When we arrived we were met at the airport by a couple of black fellows in a matching black Mercedes. I jotted down the number of the vehicle just to be on the safe side, and we were whisked off to the Togo embassy, where we met up with another batch of blacks who turned out to be the Ambassador, the first Consul, the Ambassador of Guinea and the Ambassador of Niger.

In the chat that followed, most of the conversation was in French, which Banks spoke fluently. I filled in a vacant hole in the background.

It appeared that this meeting was merely a preliminary to the main talks,and we left after the Ambassador handed me American Express cheques to the value of four hundred and forty dollars to cover the air fares, so I showed a small profit. Before I cashed the cheques I had them photo-copied. There's nothing like being careful. A further meeting had been fixed for the 19th January, again in Brussels, and during the few days interval I did some serious thinking. Up to the present I had done nothing illegal, but what was I landing myself in for?

It was all explained when Banks and I went back to Brussels on the I9th . The Ambassador disclosed that the Togo government had uncovered a plot to assassinate President Eyedema and believed that the Olympio brothers were behind it. The long and short of it was that they were willing to hire Banks to get the goods on the brothers and no holds barred. To prove they we're not kidding, they came up with a preliminary payment of £3,750 to cover expenses. Banks was well pleased and was humming "we're in the money' all the way home. I wasn't too sure about things. This kind of intrigue was outside my experience but Banks assured me that all we were doing was to act as well-paid private eyes, and there was nothing criminal in that.

Back in London I dug up a few more facts about Togo and the late President Olympio. He had been born in Lome in 1902, studied at the London School of Economics and was for a time District Manager in Togo for the United Africa Company. In 1960 he became the first President of Togoland, but he couldn't have been all that popular because, during a nine-month period in

1961, there were three attempts to kill him. His short reign came to an end in January 1963, when he was assassinated outside the gates of the US Embassy. His two sons had it away and set up an organisation called the 'Mouvement togolais pour la democratie' which had offices in Paris. They were very wealthy, though where the money came from is anybody's guess.

You can bet I wasn't too happy about the situation. I've never regarded murder as being a solution to a political problem. It seems to be a habit in the States, where they make no bones about bumping off Presidents who are surplus to requirements and, meaning no disrespect to our black brothers, they have the same ideas, or so it would seem. There's a moral in that somewhere.

The next meeting with the Togo lot had been fixed for Saturday the 22nd. Banks had brought in a couple of chaps to help out. One of them, Bobby Sewell, was a very useful boy with plenty of bottle, the other was an ex-soldier by the name of Sean Flanagan. Banks had hired a car and we drove to Dover, crossed to Calais on the ferry and drove on to Paris, where we booked in at the Residence of Charles Dullin in Montmartre. That afternoon we set out for Lille, a town on the Belgian border, where we were due to have a meet at the Holiday Inn at nine o'clock in the evening.

It was all real spy-drama stuff. The Ambassador was there along with another fellow who had flown over from Togo. They had their bodyguards close by, real pros by the look of them, who kept a watchful eye on the proceedings as we got our briefing. Our first job was to carry out surveillance on the 'Mouvement togolais' in Paris and report back on the Tuesday. It looked like money for jam when Banks asked for a further £2,000 on account of expenses and it was agreed.

We started work on the Monday. Banks had hired a van for the day, a bloody great red thing that made an ugly blotch on the landscape in the very fashionable part of Paris where the Movement's offices were situated. Bobby and I did most of the work, running off yards of film as we photographed everybody passing in and out of the building. Banks hovered in the background while Flanagan acted as a sort of messenger, losing whatever bottle he possessed in the process. At one point he hammered on the side of the van and shouted something about a bomb underneath us. I reckoned he must have watched too many James Bond films.

We went to the meet in Lille the following day and handed over the negatives of something like three hundred shots taken outside the Movement's premises. Banks copped for the promised £2,000 and we left. The idea was to go back to Paris, but we were much nearer Calais so we elected to hop on the ferry and return to London.

During the week-end I had been having some thoughts about this caper, on top of which I wasn't very pleased with the way the self-styled 'Major' Banks was handling things. I knew we were committing a minor offence under French law by snatching pictures from a concealed position, and I also knew that in France the law had a nasty habit of nicking suspects, throwing them into jail and then forgetting where they had put the key. In France, unlike the UK, you're guilty until you've been proved innocent. Anyway, over a meal and a few drinks on the boat I tackled Banks about his way of organising the affair, but I didn't get satisfactory answers.

We arrived in London and split up, with Banks saying he would be in touch as soon as he had arranged the next stage of the operation, but I had already made up my mind about that. I did not intend to put myself up front to be nicked while Banks brought up the rear and so far as his organisational abilities were concerned, I wouldn't trust him to plan a piss-up in a brewery. The upshot was that when he next phoned me I cocked a deaf 'un, and continued to do so until he got tired of it and gave up.

That was the end of my involvement with 'Major' John Banks. So far as I know he is still at it, because he had been promised a payment of $250,000 if he managed to come up with the goods on the Olympio's. Thinking things over and putting myself in Bank's shoes, I sussed out that he had made up a story about being approached by the Olympio's, taken it to the Togos and kidded them that it was true, leaked a story to the press that mercenaries were on the way to bump off Eyedema, and so constructed a scenario that was nothing more or less than a complicated confidence trick. There was obviously a cloud of suspicion surrounding the Togo camp, with nobody quite sure of what the other fellow was up to. Banks just took advantage of the situation.

CHAPTER SEVENTEEN

ELLEN:

Shortly after Joe's bit of bother at Heathrow we returned to the Dale. He had fixed us up with a very nice flat in a wide avenue just off the Portobello Road and the three of us settled in. Young Jimmy was pleased to be back once more with his mates and I was happy because I was once more among the people I had known all my life. As for Joe, he had changed to an unbelievable extent. He told me that he had finished with crime and intended to go straight. Naturally I was relieved although I did wonder what sort of work he would be suitable for. There weren't many vacancies for ex-bank robbers fresh out from a long spell in Parkhurst. What I hadn't taken into account was the fact that when Joe got a bee in his bonnet it became an obsession.

I suppose it was his contact with the journalist who did the story on the thief inside Heathrow that gave him the idea of taking up writing. He began to spend a lot of time crouched over a typewriter in the spare room, tapping away with two fingers (no journalist types properly, he told me) and, judging by the results, he didn't make a bad job of it. I read some of his work and it seemed pretty good. However, a budding writer doesn't make much money - in fact he doesn't make any money at all - and when funds began to get low he had to look around for some way of restoring the family fortunes. There was an opportunity that cropped up when he was approached by a shady character from the past who put up a proposition which, on the face of, looked quite legal. Joe took it on and made a good bit of money in the opening stages of the venture. He dropped the business like a hot brick when it looked as though it might go wrong, in the legal sense that is.

One nice thing about this new situation was that Joe took me into his confidence about what he was up to, which was a great change from the old days. Of course he wasn't completely reformed, and he couldn't break away from old associations too suddenly, but he was unavailable when there was any possibility of getting his collar felt. On the credit side he was making some good contacts in the press after the publicity of the Heathrow affair. Papers are willing to pay for good crime stories and Joe had plenty of material in that direction and, even though the Press Council had put the block on criminals being paid for their disclosures, there are ways and means of getting round that. All in all there was a fairly steady income from those sources. The days when we had to exist on the proceeds of crime were behind us.

As I have mentioned, Joe still kept contact with some of his old mates even though he wanted no part in their illegal games. He had always been on good terms with Charlie Richardson and his younger brother, and when Eddie took over a club in Catford called J. Arthur's he asked Joe if he would be interested in managing it for him. For some time I had been helping out at a cafe in St. James Road which was owned by Charlie and Eddie's father, and Eddie suggested that I ran the restaurant at J. Arthur's. The upshot was that we accepted the offer.

There has been much written about the Richardson brothers who were at one time as notorious as the Kray twins. Speaking as I find (which is how I always speak in any case) I must say that I found Eddie a very likeable man and a very easy person to work for. He gave credit where it was due and rarely criticised. Since Eddie was a face himself there were many other faces among the customers at the club and I became quite friendly with them, their wives and girl-friends. I know it must sound rather incredible but we were like one big happy family. I came to the conclusion that even the worst villain has his good side.

There was one great night at the club when Joe Longthorne gave a show, and he and Joe became great friends. They hit it off together from the start and it wasn't only because they had the same first names. Joe Longthorne had come up the hard way in his profession and had already earned the title of the Entertainer's Entertainer. After that he and my Joe were inseparable for a long time and we had many a happy party at his lovely house in Maidenhead. I remember one night when, after a good deal of booze had been consumed, all the guests jumped fully clothed into the swimming pool.

I don't want to give the impression that J. Arthur's was just a haunt of villains. However, Eddie Richardson's pals were always welcome and in general their behaviour was never out of order. Still there were occasions when things began to get out of hand, as can happen in any club. This was where Joe would step in and settle matters, not necessarily by a show of violence but by a few well-chosen words which seemed to do the trick more often than not. Joe carried a lot of weight and he was listened to.

We had been running the club for some time and it looked as though we were on a good thing, but there is no accounting for what Fate has in store. One night a gang of young toughs came in obviously out on the town for the evening. They were quite well-behaved even though they had had quite a lot to drink. The trouble started when another party of youths began to stir things up and the danger signals were out.

Normally Joe would have been alive to those danger signals but this time he was late off the mark and fighting had already started before he could take a hand in things. Normally Joe and his couple of helpers would have been more than a match for these young hoodlums, but the knifes were out and being used. Blood began to flow and some of the clients fled for their lives. Order was restored eventually but the damage was enormous. There was blood all over the place, even up the walls, and the place looked as though a wrecking crew had been at work. Fortunately nobody was killed but quite a few were seriously injured. The police and ambulances were called in and for a time it was very dodgy as some of the youths accused Joe and his helpers of strong-arm tactics. I had sheltered in the kitchen with some other members of the staff while the fights were going on.

This event was a deciding factor in our decision to leave the club. Although the police did not take any action against Joe he was in a vulnerable position since he was on licence, so we wanted to avoid further trouble by quitting. Eddie was very unhappy about this but he recognised the wisdom of our action.

We had done very well financially out of our work at the club so Joe was able to take time off to continue with his writing. His first book was almost finished and he had found a publisher for it. When it came out just before Christmas it sold quite well though it wasn't the earner he had hoped it would be. Just the same he wasn't downhearted but carried on with his next effort.

On the subject of the Richardsons there is one story which I recall very vividly. Eddie's brother Charlie was coming to the end of his sentence in prison and was allowed home leave from Coldingly. He had a great welcome party at the Sidmouth Arms, better known as Rumbles, just off the Old Kent Road, and the party was continued at J. Arthur's. He should have returned to Coldingly on the Monday but in fact he was at our home with his step-brother, also called Charlie, and a couple of mates on that evening. He didn't want to go back, which was quite understandable, but we persuaded him that it would be foolish to abscond so near the end of his sentence.

The reporters knew that Charlie was on home leave and had kept an eye on him in the hope that some sort of story would break. When he didn't report back at the appointed time the hunt was on and the press was scouring London for a sighting. A bunch of reporters were waiting outside the jail when Charlie turned up around midnight. All the doors were locked and barred and the press was treated to the sight of a prisoner hammering on the main door and begging to be let in. When you come to look at it there's a funny side to everything.

Young Jimmy had a stroke of luck about that time. A film called 'Revolution' starring Al Pacino was being made by a director by the name of Hugh Hudson and Jimmy was picked out from the whole school to play a small but important part in it. As his parents Joe and I were with him during the shooting and it was an experience for the three of us. We met Al Pacino, who had taken an instant liking to Jimmy, and also other members of the cast. It was a change from the surroundings of the Dale and we took full advantage of it. Like all good things it came to an end, but Jimmy came out of it with enough pocket money to last him for several years. His uncles, Joe's brothers, were over the moon , calling him 'our little film star', but Jimmy was not affected by all this. He did not allow it to go to his head but went back to school and carried on as though nothing had happened. When the film was released we went to the first night and hob-nobbed with the stars, though there were many disappointed people later on when the film got bad reviews. I believe the production company, Goldcrest, went out of business shortly after.

Beryl Gibbons was a well-known personality in the world of boxing. She was the landlady of the Thomas A Beckett pub in the Old Kent Road where, in the gym upstairs, many world champions had trained. We knew her very well and Joe did quite a bit of work for her on many occasions. She was on first-name terms with the leading fighters of the day, a friend of such as Henry Cooper, Mohammed Ali and many more. After twenty years in charge of the pub she fell on hard times and was in danger of being evicted by the brewers. She called on Joe for help and he did all he could to assist her but to no avail. She was in desperate financial trouble and, though she went down fighting, she was finally evicted from the pub. Joe found a squat in the neighbourhood and moved her and her belongings into it, then pestered the local authority into giving her a small flat. Shortly after moving in she died of cancer.

Talking of the world of boxing, I remember the shock we had when we heard the news of Freddie Mills' death. Joe had known him for many years. He had been world champion at his weight and, after retiring from the ring, went into the club business. The circumstances of his death were mysterious to say the least. His body had been found in his car in an alley off the charing Cross Road and there was a .22 rifle by his side. The coroner's verdict was suicide but a considerable number of people, including Joe, did not agree, in fact Joe told me in confidence that Freddie had been murdered in the course of a gangland feud. Joe said he knew who had committed the crime and the killer had been paid a thousand pounds for the deed.

I have mentioned previously that Joe was very conscious of his duty to his family and never failed to see that we never went short of anything. Our daughter was now happily married with children of her own, making Joe a grandfather which pleased him more than a little. He took this responsibility seriously, making sure that they had presents on their birthdays and at Christmas. The day to day business of living did not come all that cheap, but the household bills were paid promptly and if I wanted anything in the way of furnishings for the flat the cash was always available.

There was a time when Joe had an answer to any financial troubles. He would go out and rob a bank. Not any more. He stuck to his promise to go straight and grafted honestly for his money. There were times when he was approached by some of his old mates to make one in some criminal exploit or other, but he stuck to his guns and turned them down. He didn't blank out his old associates, he couldn't in all conscience do that, but he just wasn't available for anything criminal.

He was still plugging away with his writing and also doing work for the papers who often called him in to help with their investigations into various aspects of crime. Of course he had to be very careful because he held to the opinion that a grass is the lowest form of animal life and he stopped short of pointing a finger at any of his old friends. For the rest he used his knowledge of the underworld to gather material which he used in his books which he called 'faction', a mixture of fact and fiction.

In the late eighties we were pretty well off by our standards. We didn't have stacks of readies hidden under mattresses or anything like that but enough cash was coming in to make life comfortable. Joe had three of his books published with a couple more in the pipeline, and they returned a small and steady income. However he was still searching for a means of providing for the time when we could both retire. Jimmy had left school and was making his own way in the world and doing a good job of it. Joe was figuring a way of 'hitting the jackpot' as he termed it.

This was the time of the great property boom and fortunes were being made in the housing market. When Joe was approached by a fellow called Freddie Nash and invited to join him in his property deals he saw the possibilities and decided to have some of it. Freddie had a slightly shady past, but then who hasn't, and in any case Joe was well able to take care of himself.

Freddie had certainly done well for himself. He had a lovely house down at Lewes, rode around in a Rolls and, through a chain of companies in which he held a controlling interest, bought up properties with sitting tenants. He then got the tenants out either by offering them money or employing other means, some of them being what I would call dodgy even though they were legal. When the properties were put on the market with vacant possession they fetched considerably higher prices, and that's where the fortunes were being made. On the face of it everything looked on the level but when I met some of Freddie's helpers I wasn't so sure.

As a qualified bookeeper I was very useful when Joe took over some of the Nash properties. I had a sketchy knowledge of company law and kept a weather eye on any commitments that were being entered into. Freddie was a very clever man and was as cunning as a bag of rats, plus he had a bunch of people round him who weren't exactly idiots. Colin Trundell was an estate agent who got away with something like a couple of million and later had it away to Malta on a moody passport which he got by representing himself as somebody who was already dead. He copied details, date of birth etc, from a gravestone in a cemetery. Then a friend of Joe's, an alleged expert in mortgage fraud, who was, like Freddie, a member of the hunt- Was maybe responsible for frauds totalling over two billion.

Mike Logan handled the tough end of the business such as harassing tenants to get them out of some of the properties. He was a very hard man who played some pretty dirty tricks such as flooding their rooms and slinging their furniture out on the streets. Another couple who were in it up to their necks were an ex-policeman, and a well-known horse trainer. A fellow who was as dodgy as his peculiar name.

Joe broke up with the gang when Freddie tried to have him over in a deal about a local property. There was a settlement which worked to Joe's advantage financially and that was that. In my opinion he was well out of it.

This about wraps up my story. My husband is now a moderately successful author of five published works and a couple of others in the pipeline. One of his books is being considered as the subject for a major film. Our children, Kim and young Jimmy, are doing well and the only cloud on the horizon is the state of the nation, and we can't do very much about that. I have no complaints about my life. If I had to live it all over again I wouldn't change anything. A quotation comes to mind which I read somewhere, the colonel's lady and Judy O'Grady are sisters under the skin. The gangster's lady fits into this somehow or other. One last word. I remember when Maggie (now Lady) Thatcher was slung out of 10 Downing Street. As she got into her official car she uttered a few words. 'It's a funny old world,' she said. I couldn't agree with her more.

BORN ROTTEN.

JOE CANNON.

This bizarre novel is a powerful, gripping and exciting
story which tells of the bruitality and violence of London's underworld as it is today.
Joey Bello, the anti-hero described by the title, takes
the reader into the criminal haunts of London's Soho,
the subculture of Notting Hill where racial tensions fuel
sporadic outbreaks of violence, the eerie night-life of
the West End, and the strange other world of the expa-
triate villian basking in the Spanish sun.
As the Bello saga unfolds, the reader is transported into
the battle-ground of international crime, where billions
of pounds, dollars and other currencies swell the pockets of traffickers in drugs and vice, where conspiracy,
extortion corruption and murder are commonplace. Here
the Mafia, a criminal octupus, spreads its tentacles
worldwide.
BORN ROTTEN throws a searchlight on international
crime and in doing so opens up a new era in crime
fiction.

Paperback price £4.50 net U.K.

YELLOW BRICK PUBLISHERS. 2, Lonsdale Road,
Queens Park. London . NW6 6RD.

ENGLAND'S TOUGHEST VILLIAN.

JOE CANNON.

Gripping, exciting, and often horrifying, this is the
story of Joey Bello, an ex-criminal, who wages his own
personal war against corruption in the highest places:
the untouchable echolons of our own police force and
especially the Mafia.
Joey Bello fights on his terms. He meets violence with
violence, bruitality with bruitality.
ENGLAND'S TOUGHEST VILLIAN opens a window
into the sub-culture of the underworld, introducing the
reader to a side of life which he would ordinarily and
otherwise not see: a world of theives jargon and evil
deeds, where danger lurks in dark corners and where the
threat of death is ever-present: a world in which a sawn-
off shotgun is no respecter of persons: where a .45
automatic is a great leveller.

Paperback price £4.50 net U.K.

YELLOW BRICK PUBLISHERS. 2, Lonsdale Road,
Queens Park, London. NW6 6RD.

JUDGE ME NOT.

JOE CANNON.

In this book, the final volume of the trilogy following
BORN ROTTEN and ENGLAND'S TOUGHEST VIL-
LIAN, the saga of Joey Bello continues.
Here the author draws on his considerable knowledge of
sophisticated crime to give a picture of computer frauds
carried out by Bello and his confederates. While not
being a guide to the essential elements of this type of
crime, the fiction presented here has a basis in fact, as
any computer hacker will know.
A chapter of the book is devoted to a fictionalised
account of the probable circumstances surrounding the
murder on the Costa del Sol of Great Train Robber
Charlie Wilson. Amid a welter of speculation, the author's informed opinion is as good as any and better
than most. He opens a window on criminal activity
which has hitherto been securely locked and bolted.

Paperback price £4.50 net U.K.

YELLOW BRICK PUBLISHERS. 2, Lonsdale Road,
Queens Park, London. NW6 6RD.

CARDBOARD CITY.

JOE CANNON.

Tommy Hutton was a happy man. He had a good job and a comfortable home where he lived with his wife and infant daughter. When wife and child were killed in a train accident, Tommy turned to drink. One day he burned his house to the ground in a drunken rage and set out for London. Now a confirmed alcoholic, he haunted the public houses of Bayswater. When his money ran out, he found refuge among London's homeless beneath the arches of Waterloo Bridge.

The story of his experiences is set against the background of CARDBOARD CITY, a community of the homeless and the hopeless where society's outcasts sleep in cardboard boxes. It is a harrowing story marked by scenes of violence, but in the end he conquers his addiction and dedicates himself to helping the unfortunates who were instrumental in bringing him face to face with reality.

Paperback price £4.95 net U.K.

YELLOW BRICK PUBLISHERS. 2, Lonsdale Road, Queens Park, London. NW6 6RD.